PENGUIN BOOKS

The Soul of Medicine

Peter Adams is a Registered Homoeopath and has been in practice since 1984. He is joint owner of the Stroud Natural Health Clinic which provides twelve different complementary therapies. A graduate of Oxford University, he is married with two daughters, and lives in Gloucestershire.

At one stage in his work as a homoeopath he needed to understand his role as a healer in a deeper and more soulful way. This book is a result of that investigation.

He is also the author of *Homoeopathy: Natural Medicine for the Whole Person*, an introduction to understanding and using homoeopathy.

PETER ADAMS

The Soul of Medicine

PENGUIN BOOKS

PENGUIN BOOKS

Published by the Penguin Group
Penguin Books Ltd, 27 Wrights Lane, London w8 5tz, England
Penguin Putnam Inc., 375 Hudson Street, New York, New York 10014, USA
Penguin Books Australia Ltd, Ringwood, Victoria, Australia
Penguin Books Canada Ltd, 10 Alcorn Avenue, Toronto, Ontario, Canada m4v 3b2
Penguin Books (NZ) Ltd, Private Bag 102902, NSMC, Auckland, New Zealand

Penguin Books Ltd, Registered Offices: Harmondsworth, Middlesex, England

First published 1999
1 3 5 7 9 10 8 6 4 2

Copyright © Peter Adams, 1999
All rights reserved

The moral right of the author has been asserted

The acknowledgements on pp. 289–93 constitute an extension of this copyright page

Set in 10/14 pt PostScript Monotype Gill Sans Light and 11/14 pt PostScript Monotype Sabon
Typeset by Rowland Phototypesetting Ltd, Bury St Edmunds, Suffolk
Made and printed in Great Britain by Clays Ltd, St Ives plc

For Eve

I am not a mechanism, an assembly of various sections.
And it is not because the mechanism is working wrongly, that I am ill.
I am ill because of wounds to the soul, to the deep emotional self . . .
D. H. Lawrence (1996)

The great malady of the twentieth century, implicated in all of our troubles
and affecting us individually and socially, is loss of soul. When soul is
neglected, it doesn't just go away; it appears symptomatically in obsessions,
addictions, violence, and loss of meaning. Thomas Moore (1992)

> It is difficult
> to get the news from poems
> yet men die miserably every day
> for lack
> of what is found there.
> William Carlos Williams (1951)

Contents

CONTENTS

PART II

AFFLICTIONS FROM THE CRADLE
TO THE GRAVE

PART III

GRANT US HEALTH WE PRAY —
THE MYSTERIES OF HEALING

Introduction

This anthology is intended to be a source of comfort, inspiration and healing for patients and their healers. Illness is an experience that everyone shares at one time or another. Whether you, the reader, are a tired doctor at the end of a busy day or a patient who has just been diagnosed as having a serious illness and are now seeking an understanding of what is happening to you, I hope that you will find something appealing and moving in this book. Whether you are an exhausted carer overcome by the task of looking after someone who is seriously ill, or you are the one having to look death in the face, there may be encouragement and solace here. If you are a student of acupuncture needing inspiration for your studies or simply someone who is becoming aware of the toll that life is taking on your health, I hope that this book will be able to offer you something. You can dip into it for a few minutes here and there, or read it from cover to cover.

Illness opens up new experience for the soul as well as the body. The pieces of writing in this book will map out step by step the way illness touches our hearts and moves our souls. Perhaps the writings can help to guide the patient, carer and healer, so that rather than lurching through illness clumsily, we can take each step with as much grace and assurance as the circumstances allow.

The first part of the book, ' "When I Was Sick and Lay A-Bed": The Experience of Illness', takes us through the experience of illness from the first disturbance of our normal and healthy lives, through the horrors and fears which accompany illness and the search for healing, to the new healed self that can emerge from the struggle. Also covered here are the role of the doctor (or healer of whatever kind), and the qualities and powers which he or she needs.

The central part, 'Afflictions from the Cradle to the Grave', is made up of pieces of writing about a selection of illnesses and states of body and mind. This includes specific medical conditions, from fevers and colds to anorexia and cancer. But disease is also 'dis-ease', a less specific condition, a state of being which is not easily measured. It is hidden within us and exerts a powerful influence on our health. For this reason I include in this section descriptions of the states of dis-ease of heart and soul such as grief, insomnia, obesity and stuttering. There is a section which has writers' comments on the enormity of straightforward physical pain.

The final part of the book, 'Grant Us Health, We Pray – The Mysteries of Healing', goes into the more mysterious realms of sickness and healing. Here you will find stories and myths about the gods and goddesses of healing, the contribution that shamanism can make and extracts from religious books and mythology. The writings of mystics and saints can help us to find some religious or spiritual meaning in suffering.

Doctors often make brief appearances in times of crisis in many of our well-known and well-loved stories. Their part in the narrative is often to announce a turn in the tide of events from good to bad, from abundance and happiness to privation and misery. In a few writers, especially the poets, there is an exploration of the personal experience of sickness and pain, how it changes people, and how the human spirit reaches out in search of healing.

Poetry, in both the reading and the writing thereof, is essentially a healing process. It heals by lifting human suffering out of meaninglessness into beauty; the pain of life becomes a prayer to and for life. John Stuart Mill, the nineteenth-century champion of utilitarianism, changed his beliefs after a time of suicidal depression. He came to acknowledge the need to cultivate feelings and he came to love poetry: 'What made Wordsworth's poems a medicine for my state of mind was that they expressed not mere outward beauty but states of feeling, and of thought coloured by feeling . . .'[1]

An anthology can be a medicine chest: 'A well-chosen anthology is a complete dispensary of medicine for the more common

1. J. S. Mill, *Autobiography*, 1873

x

mental disorders, and may be used as much for prevention as cure.'[1]

The psychologist C. G. Jung also describes the healing power of artistic activity. All the creative arts are able to heal individuals and whole societies, for the artist 'evokes in us all those beneficent forces that ever and anon have enabled humanity to find a refuge from every peril and to outlive the longest night.'[2]

'The creative process . . . makes it possible for us to find our way back to the deepest springs of life. Therein lies the social significance of art: it is constantly at work educating the spirit of the age, conjuring up the forms in which the age is most lacking. The unsatisfied yearning of the artist reaches back to the primordial image in the unconscious which is best fitted to compensate the inadequacy and one-sidedness of the present.'[3]

Part of the healing we need when we are ill is to be able to express our suffering and receive comfort. We also need to be able to make some sense of our problems, and to relate them to something greater than ourselves. If there is something we can believe in, if there is some hope or some meaning or just some larger frame of reference, pain and sickness are easier to bear. Human beings instinctively seek and appreciate meaning; finding a meaningful context for suffering gives us a way of coping with it. This book contains the voices of many writers concerning pain and illness, whether physical or psychological or spiritual, and they relate it to the great questions of life and its purpose. I hope these voices will be a source of comfort and healing, as they reveal to us that others have also been tried and troubled by illness and have left us some of their wisdom.

These voices will come from many different ages and cultures, and will express many different beliefs about health and disease. This applies especially to the extracts taken from medical, sociological and psychological works. In addition to bringing comfort they may well raise some questions and perhaps introduce a new understanding of

1. Robert Graves, *On English Poetry*, Heinemann, 1922
2. C. G. Jung, *The Spirit in Man, Art and Literature* (Collected Works, vol. 15), translated by R. F. C. Hull, Routledge & Kegan Paul, 1966
3. ibid.

healing. The many responses to illness, from religious to scientific, as exemplified by the shaman and the surgeon, will all be present in these pages.

In all illnesses our souls are troubled, and they need healing as well as our bodies. Many of the sicknesses which are increasing in our times, such as anxiety, depression, addictions, obsessions and violence, are soul sicknesses. Poetry and the kind of writing to be found in this book are helpful to a troubled soul, and sometimes have great healing power. Art and science can complement each other. This quotation concerns a research psychiatrist: 'Before he begins new research, he reads to see whether poets and artists have already expressed the same ideas. If they have, he proceeds, knowing he is on the right track.'[1]

Wordsworth here gives poetry great importance: 'The man of Science seeks truth as a remote and unknown benefactor; he cherishes and loves it in his solitude: the Poet, singing a song in which all human beings join with him, rejoices in the presence of truth as our visible friend and hourly companion. Poetry is the breath and finer spirit of all knowledge: It is the impassioned expression which is in the countenance of all Science.'[2]

This book will also emphasize the non-scientific, poetic and spiritual sides of illness and healing, without in any way denying that a scientific approach to medicine is essential. The intention is only 'to illustrate that there can be tools other than scientific ones for dealing with the sickness, anxieties, and tears of human life'.[3]

The rigid division of body from mind, science from religion and matter from spirit is fading. Scientists are becoming mystical, and beliefs about disease are changing too. A cross-fertilizing relationship between soul and medicine is a healing for humanity and an enrichment of our medical practice. This anthology is a contribution to our endeavours to bring science and the arts closer together.

1. Bernie S. Siegel, *Love, Medicine and Miracles*, Harper & Row, 1986
2. William Wordsworth, Preface to *The Lyrical Ballads*, 1802
3. R. S. Downie, Preface to R. S. Downie, ed., *The Healing Arts: An Oxford Illustrated Anthology*, OUP, 1995

A Note to the Reader

'Illness', 'sickness', and 'disease' all mean the same thing in this book, and refer to that condition of 'not being well' that is shared by everyone who is ill, whatever the diagnosis may be. The word 'healer' is also given the widest possible meaning – any health professional or amateur, of whatever system of treatment. The urge to heal is shared by all these, and it is movements of soul such as that urge which are the concerns of this book. I use all these terms to evoke an experience rather than to give accurate descriptions.

We are all 'the patient', because we are all in need of medical help at some time. It is only necessary to sprain an ankle to become, if only for a moment, helpless and crying out for aid. We are all 'the healer' too, because we all at some time feel for someone who is suffering. We need only read a newspaper article or hear that a friend is ill for our caring side to be activated.

Anything expressed in poetry has extra power and becomes more persuasive. But we must also remember that making something rhyme doesn't necessarily make it universally true. And poetry is not a substitute for medical treatment. The approach to illness in this book can be fruitful if it is taken in moderation, with circumspection, and with appropriate health care.

If any readers know of other pieces of writing on the subject I would be grateful to hear about them. Please address letters to me, care of the publisher.

Where bibliographical details are known a date appears at the end of the quote, which cross-refers to the Bibliography on pp. 275–89. The date given is not necessarily the date of composition, but is the date of publication of the edition cited.

PART I
'When I Was Sick and Lay A-Bed'
THE EXPERIENCE OF ILLNESS

I

The Body in Illness

A man is flesh and blood and brittle bones,
The flesh can sing or flood the day with groans . . .
S. I. Henderson Smith

Illness in Literature

Virginia Woolf has the first words, because the long and glorious opening sentence of her essay 'On Being Ill' sets the right tone for the beginning of this book:

Considering how common illness is, how tremendous the spiritual change that it brings, how astonishing, when the lights of health go down, the undiscovered countries that are then disclosed, what wastes and deserts of the soul a slight attack of influenza brings to view, what precipices and lawns sprinkled with bright flowers a little rise of temperature reveals, what ancient and obdurate oaks are uprooted in us by the act of sickness, how we go down into the pit of death and feel the waters of annihilation close above our heads and wake thinking to find ourselves in the presence of the angels and the harpers when we have a tooth out and come to the surface in the dentist's arm chair and confuse his 'Rinse the mouth – rinse the mouth' with the greeting of the deity stooping from the door of Heaven to welcome us – when we think of this, as we are so frequently forced to think of it, it becomes strange indeed that illness has not taken its place with love and battle and jealousy among the prime themes of literature. Novels, one would have thought, would have been devoted to influenza; epics to typhoid; odes to pneumonia; lyrics to toothache. Virginia Woolf (1967)

This book will collect together pieces of writing that concentrate on the experience of illness. Although illness is not a dominant theme in most books there is still plenty of material to choose from, and some of it is the most exquisite writing in the world's literature.

The intention is to 'push the pause button' on illness – in these pieces the writer does not announce the fate of the patient and return quickly to the narrative, but stays at the bedside and turns his or her attention to the inner world of the person set apart by illness. In medical terms, we are not going to move on towards the diagnosis and the prognosis. We are going to linger with the symptoms themselves in order to become more conscious of what it is like to be 'a patient'.

There is a temptation in our high-speed rational age, where illness is concerned, to get the problem out of the way and return to normal as quickly as possible. This book reins in this urge and encourages slowness and receptivity, which are soul qualities. The journey through each section in the book is a stage in developing a soul experience of illness. Each stage is a leisurely visit to a state of being that is induced by illness, in the belief that lingering there can be a healing experience.

The Body in Health: The Flesh is Singing

Every healthy man is a king. Gaelic proverb

The following passages celebrate the healthy human body. In the first the human body is compared to a house:

The house I live in contains a curious apparatus, which may be compared to a great bellows, by whose wonderful operation the blood is cleansed and purified. This is contained in the upper storey, and fills nearly the whole of it, leaving but a small chamber on one side for the heart. It blows its blast at the rate of twenty or twenty-five in a minute in an adult person, and at a still greater rate in children; and it continues these blasts, whether standing or sitting, sleeping or waking, as long as we live. I refer, as you will readily perceive, to the lungs . . .

So numerous are the pipes and cells in the lungs, that it is commonly considered that the extent of mucous membrane which lines them must be equal at least to the extent of the skin, which is, in a middling sized adult, about fifteen square feet. Thomas Girtin (1872)

These lines were written after Harvey's discovery of the circulation of the blood:

> The salient point, so first is called the heart,
> Shap'd and suspended with amazing art,
> By turns dilated, and by turns comprest,
> Expels, and entertains the purple guest.
> It sends from out its left contracted side
> Into th'arterial tube its vital pride:
> Which tube, prolong'd but little from its source,
> Parts its wide trunk, and takes a double course;
> One channel to the head its path directs,
> One to th'inferior limbs its path inflects.
> Both smaller by degrees, and smaller grow,
> And on the parts, thro' which they branching go,
> A thousand secret, subtle pipes bestow.
> From which by num'rous convolutions wound,
> Wrapt with th'attending nerve, and twisted round,
> The complicated knots and kernels rise,
> Of various figures, and of various size.
> Th'arterial ducts, when thus involved, produce
> Unnumber'd glands, and of important use.
> But after, as they farther progress make,
> The appellation of a vein they take.
> For though th'arterial pipes themselves extend
> In smallest branches, yet they never end:
> The same continu'd circling channels run
> Back to the heart, where first their course begun.
> Sir Richard Blackmore (1712)

And here the nerves are described in the same way – as travellers sent out from the centre on a journey to the periphery, and back again to the brain:

Last, to enjoy her sense of feeling
(A thing she much delights to deal in)
A thousand little nerves she sends;
And these in gratitude again
Return their spirits to the brain . . .
Matthew Prior (1718)

The Body as Microcosm

If anything is sacred the human body is sacred.
Walt Whitman (1853)

The seventeenth-century poet George Herbert describes how the human body is greater than the sum of its parts. He goes on to say that the body is a microcosm, having correspondence with the planets:

Man is all symmetry,
Full of proportions, one limb to another,
And all to all the world besides;
Each part may call the furthest brother,
For head with foot hath private amity,
And both with moons and tides.

Nothing hath got so far,
But man hath caught and kept it as his prey;
His eyes dismount the highest star;
He is in little all the sphere;
Herbs gladly cure our flesh, because that they
Find their acquaintance there.
George Herbert (1633)

Paracelsus is the main medical spokesperson for this view, the doctrine of correspondences. An outspoken, bombastic, rebellious, unconventional healer of the sixteenth century, he inspires medical thinkers to this day. Here he connects medicine with astrology:

The body of a man is his house: the architect who builds it is the astral world. The carpenters are at one time Jupiter, at another Venus; at one time Taurus, at another Orion. Man is a sun and a moon and a heaven filled with stars; the world is a man, and the light of the sun and the stars is his body . . . Paracelsus (in Hartmann, 1973)

Here in this body are the sacred rivers: here are the sun and moon as well as all pilgrimage places . . . I have not encountered another temple as blissful as my own body. Saraha

Remembering the Body

At certain moments my body is illuminated . . . Suddenly I see into myself . . . I can make out the depth of the layers of my flesh. Paul Valéry (1973)

> Only close your eyes and you seem a forest
> Of dense vegetation, and the lurking beast
> That in the night springs from the cover
> Tears with tiger's mouth your living creatures . . .
> Rock-face of bone, alluvium of cartilage
> Remote from man as the surface of the moon
> Are vast and unexplored interior desert ranges,
> Grow like unreaped fields of waving corn.
> Kathleen Raine (1949)

We all share in the experience of the body in sickness, yet we do not talk about it much. The following piece of writing describes how literature neglects our sensation of our bodies:

. . . with a few exceptions – De Quincey attempted something of the sort in *The Opium Eater*; there must be a volume or two about disease scattered through the pages of Proust – literature does its best to maintain that its concern is with the mind; and that the body is a sheet of plain glass through which the soul looks straight and clear, and, save for one or two passions such as desire and greed, is null and negligible and non-existent. On the contrary, the very opposite is true. All day, all night the body intervenes; blunts or sharpens, colours or discolours, turns to wax in the warmth of June, hardens to tallow in the murk of February. The creature within can only gaze through the pane – smudged or rosy; it cannot separate off from the body like the sheath of a knife or the pod of a pea for a single instant; it must go through the whole unending procession of changes, heat and cold, comfort and discomfort, hunger and satisfaction, health and illness, until there comes the inevitable catastrophe; the body smashes itself to smithereens, and the soul, it is said, escapes. But of all this daily drama of the body there is no record. People write always of the doings of the mind; the thoughts that come into it; its noble plans; how the mind has civilized the universe. They show it ignoring the body in the philosopher's turret; or kicking the body, like an old leather football, across leagues of snow and desert in the pursuit of conquest or discovery. Those great wars which the body wages, with the mind a slave to it, in the solitude of the bedroom against the assault of fever or the oncome of melancholia, are neglected. Virginia Woolf (1967)

It is not only in literature that our bodies are neglected. We tend to be impatient with any pain or dysfunction and suppress it instantly. Let's now consider our experience of the physical body, in illness and in health, a little more:

The immediate experience of the human body is something which we take for granted. We perceive and act with it and become fully aware of its presence only when it is injured, or when it goes wrong. Even then the subjective experience of the body is usually incoherent and perplexing . . . Jonathan Miller (1978)

To a large extent the body is a closed system, adapting and responding without our conscious intervention:

The inside of the body – blood vessels, heart, intestine, lungs and bladder – is literally studded with instruments capable of registering changes in pressure, temperature and chemical composition. But none of these meters has any dials: they are not meant to be read by human consciousness, but are linked up with the reflex systems which obey automatically . . . When you start to exercise, your heart automatically speeds up in order to supply the working muscles with the blood they need. But you don't make the decision to speed up your heart. Jonathan Miller (1978)

In health we have only a limited awareness of our bodies. This leaves us free to give our attention to the main concerns of our lives. Our bodies are quiescent carriers of consciousness, stalwart workhorses obeying our will. Through them we are able to have impact on our surroundings, and adapt the world to our design.

Body is between consciousness and the world. Merleau-Ponty (1962)

The thickness of the body is the opening into the world. Ronald Schenk (1986)

The hand is the visible part of the brain. Immanuel Kant

At the end of the mind, the body. But at the end of the body, the mind. Paul Valéry (1973)

Psyche and body react sympathetically to each other, it seems to me. A change in the state of the psyche produces a change in the structure of the body and conversely a change in the structure of the body produces a change in the state of the psyche. Aristotle

Body and Soul

Body is a portion of the soul discern'd by the five senses. William Blake (1977)

What is the relationship between body and soul?

According to the law of the Most High the body is the work of the soul. It creates its own covering and hammers it from within outwards, like a goldsmith making a vessel decorated in relief. Leonardo da Vinci

The red jellies within you or within me, the bones and the marrow
    in the bones,
The exquisite realization of health;
O I say these are not the parts and poems of the body only, but
    of the soul,
O I say now these are the soul!
Walt Whitman (1853)

In the following dialogue between soul and body, the soul is an unwilling prisoner in the body:

SOUL

O, who shall from this dungeon raise
A soul, enslaved so many ways,
With bolts of bones, that fettered stands
In feet, and manacled in hands.
Here blinded with an eye; and there
Deaf with the drumming of an ear,
A soul hung up, as 'twere, in chains
Of nerves, and arteries, and veins.
Tortured, besides each other part,
In a vain head, and double heart.

BODY

O, who shall me deliver whole,
From bonds of this tyrannic soul,
Which, stretched upright, impales me so,
That mine own precipice I go;
And warms and moves this needless frame
(A fever could but do the same),
And, wanting where its spite to try,
Has made me live to let me die,
A body that could never rest,
Since this ill spirit is possessed.

Andrew Marvell (1681)

A human being occupies a body but is not just that body:

This frame compacted with transcendent skill,
Of moving joints, obedient to my will:
Nurs'd from the fruitful glebe, like yonder tree,
Waxes and wastes; I call it mine not me:
New matters still the mould'ring mass sustains,
The mansion chang'd, the tenant still remains . . .

John Arbuthnot (1734)

If our illness takes up residence in our bodies and comes to our attention from there, then our bodies are no longer transparent to our experience.

We start to feel the complexity of our anatomies. They start to make their presence felt, block our intentions and become a hindrance.

Body is the darkness upon which experience is inscribed. Maurice Merleau-Ponty (1962)

> But now afflictions bow me down to earth . . .
> Suspends what nature gave me at my birth . . .
> Till that which suits a part infects the whole,
> And now is almost grown the habit of my soul.
>
> S. T. Coleridge (1802)

Who will rid me of the body, of this death? My body is chained to me – a dead weight. It is my warder. I can do nothing without first consulting it and seeking its permission. I jeer at its grotesqueness. I chafe at the things it binds on me. On this bully I am dependent for everything the world can give me. W. N. P. Barbellion (1948)

Also the body can be an anchor or security if we surrender to it:

Illness taught me that beyond anything I can do, the body simply is. In the wisdom of the body's being I find myself, over and over again. Arthur Frank (1991)

We start to wonder how our bodies work:

> Knowest thou but how the stone doth enter in
> The bladder's cave, and never break the skin?
> Know'st thou how blood, which to the heart doth flow,
> Doth one ventricle to th'other go?
> And for the putrid stuff which thou dost spit,
> Know'st thou how thy lungs have attracted it?
>
> Ben Jonson (1616)

Exploring Within: The Body and Surgery

We know a staggering amount about the body and how it works. Yet we still feel wonder and horror when confronted with blood and guts:

How often, when operating in some deep, dark wound, along the course of some great vein, with thin walls, alternately distended and flaccid with the vital current – how often have I dreaded that some unfortunate struggle of the patient would deviate the knife a little from its proper course, and that I who fain would be the deliverer should involuntarily become the executioner, seeing my patient perish in my hands by the most appalling form of death! Valentine Mott (1865)

Only one neat square of Jenny's body remained uncovered and the neat square showed up distinctly against the white clipped towels because the square was covered in a fine bright yellow. The picric acid did that. It was inside this square that everything was taking place, inside the square that Hilda used her instruments, her smooth rubbery hands.

First there came the incision, yes, the incision came first. The warm shining lancet drew a slow firm line across the bright yellow skin and the skin took lips and smiled in a wide red smile. Little jets of red spouted from the smiling red lips and Hilda's black hands moved and moved and a ring of shiny forceps lay all round the wound. A. J. Cronin (1937)

Richard Selzer, writer and surgeon, confesses to an uneasy feeling about his searches inside the body. Opening the body for surgery becomes a violation of a sacred place. His words give us a strong sense of the mystery of living tissue and raise the question of something there which eludes our exploration:

Even now, after so many journeys within, so much exploration, I feel the same sense that one must not gaze into the body, the same irrational fear that it is an evil deed for which punishment awaits. Richard Selzer (1982)

The surgeon knows the landscape of the brain, yet does not know how a thought is made. Man has grown envious of this mystery. He would master and subdue it electronically. He would construct a computer to rival and surpass the brain . . . There are men who implant electrodes into the brain, that part where anger is kept – the rage centre, they call it. They press a button, and the furious bull halts in mid-charge, and lopes amiably to nuzzle his matador. Anger has turned to sweet compliance. Others sever whole tracts of brain cells with their knives, to mollify the insane. Here is surgery grown violent as rape. These men cannot know the brain. They have not the heart for it.

I last saw the brain in the emergency room. I wiped it from the shoulder of a young girl to make her smashed body more presentable to her father. Now I stand with him by the stretcher. We are arm in arm, like brothers. All at once there is that terrible silence of discovery. I glance at him, follow his gaze and see that there is more brain upon her shoulder, newly slipped from the cracked skull. He bends forwards a bit. He must make certain. It is her brain! I watch the knowledge expand upon his face, so like hers. I too stare at the fragment flung wetly, now drying beneath the bright lights of the emergency room, its cargo of thoughts evaporating from it, mingling for this little time with his, with mine, before dispersing in the air. Richard Selzer (1982)

The Body as a Stranger

This body, then, which hovered before him, this individual and living I, was a monstrous multiplicity of breathing and self-nourishing individuals ... some only understood how to change their shape or produce digestive secretions. Thomas Mann (1996)

In the recesses of the physical body I search for the philosopher's stone. I know it is there, hidden in the deepest, dampest cul-de-sac. It awaits discovery. To find it would be like the harnessing of fire. It would illuminate the world. Richard Selzer (1982)

After looking into his own body through the most up-to-date equipment, the following medical writer has great respect for the body's intelligence, but feels no closer to it:

I have seen a lot of my inner self, more than most people, and you'd think I would have gained some new insight, even some sense of illumination, but I am as much in the dark as ever. I do not feel connected to myself in any new way. Indeed, if anything the distance seems to have increased, and I am personally more a dualism than ever, made up of structure after structure over which I have no say at all. I have the feeling now that if I were to keep at it, looking everywhere with lenses and bright lights, even into the ventricles of my brain (which is a technical feasibility if I wanted to try it), or inside the arteries of the heart (another easy technique these days), I would be brought no closer to myself. I exist, I'm sure of that, but not in the midst of all that soft machinery. If I am, as I suppose is the case at bottom, an assemblage of electromagnetic particles, I now doubt that there is any centre, any passenger compartment, any private green room where I am to be found in residence. I conclude that the arrangement runs itself, beyond my management, needing repairs by experts from time to time, but by and large running well, and I am glad I don't have to worry about the details. If I were really at the controls, in full charge, keeping track of everything, there would be a major train wreck within seconds.

And I do not at all resent any of the parts for going wrong. On the contrary, having seen what they are up against, I have more respect for them than I had before. I tip my hat to all of them, and I'm glad I'm here outside, wherever that is. Lewis Thomas (1992)

This passage says that an immortal spirit inhabits the body, though not any single part:

One of the chambers in the interior of the brain was supposed, by the philosopher Descartes, to be the particular residence of the spiritual inhabitant; and many other parts, by fanciful speculators, have been assigned as seats of the soul. These theories have long since been abandoned as untenable; and I can assure the reader with certainty, that my immortal spirit does not reside exclusively in any one part. It lives in all parts of brain, spinal marrow, and the nervous system in general, and they may all be considered as simply an extension of one great and important central communication, which forms the connection between the material organization and the mental phenomena. Thomas Girtin (1872)

2

The Soul in Illness

Your facts are useful, and yet they are not my dwelling-place.
Walt Whitman (1871)

The Undiscovered Country: Illness as a Different Reality

The art of being ill is no easy one to learn . . . Julia Duckworth Stephen
(1987)

We can see illness as a band of human experience which is far removed
from everyday reality. The sick are attuned to a different wavelength of life:

Illness is the night side of life, a more onerous citizenship. Everyone
who is born holds dual citizenship, in the kingdom of the well and in
the kingdom of the sick. Susan Sontag (1978)

In the world of sickness we are ravaged by elemental forces:

> Motions and perturbations of the minds,
> Resemble tempests, thunder, lightning, wind
> Which in our aery region do arise,
> To cloud the mind, and so obscure the skies . . .
> Tumours like meteors in our bodies rise,
> The exhalations of impurities:
> And in a colic or hysteric fit,
> We feel pent wind an earthquake make in it . . .
> Our mind the day is, and our flesh the night,
> Death is but darkness, and our life the light.
> John Collop (1660)

For the Eskimo, when one falls ill, one takes on a new name, a new diseased personality. To get over a disease, one must quite literally 'get over it' by transcending it, that is, by dying. The only hope for cure lies in the death of the ill personality. James Hillman (1964)

'When the Lights of Health Go Down': The Onset of Illness

Something startles me where I thought I was safest.
Walt Whitman (1871)

To lose one's health renders science null, art inglorious, strength effortless, wealth useless and eloquence powerless. Herophilus
This is how we cross over into the world of the sick:

After a lifetime
a steady heartbeat may start to flap
like a flock of rooks stuck in a chimney
a car may plough through a bus queue
a millpond become a whirlpool
mountains erupt.
Cicely Herbert (1992)

The first symptom of returning disease, of going wrong, is *the sense* that something is going wrong. This point cannot be emphasized too strongly. The patient does not experience a precisely formulated and neatly tabulated list of symptoms, but an intuitive, unmistakable sense that 'there is something the matter'. It is not reasonable to expect him to be able to define exactly what is the matter, for it is the indefinable sense of 'wrongness' that indicates, to him and to us, the *general* nature of his malaise: the sense of wrongness which he experiences is, so to speak, his first glimpse of a *wrong world*. Oliver Sacks (1973)

Affliction is anonymous before all things; it deprives its victims of their personalities and makes them into things. It is indifferent; and it is the coldness of this indifference – a metallic coldness – that freezes all those it touches right to the depths of their souls. They will never find warmth again. They will never believe any more that they are anyone. Simone Weil (1979)

This 'wrong world' torments us:

> . . . Stretch'd on our downy, yet uneasy beds,
> We change our pillows, and we raise our heads;
> From side to side, in vain, for rest we turn,
> With cold we shiver, or with heat we burn;
> Of night impatient, we demand the day:
> The day arrives and for the night we pray;
> The night and day successive come and go,
> Our lasting pains no interruption know.
>
> Sir Richard Blackmore (1712)

> Shoulders and loins
> Ache . . . !
> Ache, and the mattress,
> Runs into boulders and hummocks,
> Glows like a kiln . . .
>
> W. E. Henley (1992)

There can be a hallucinogenic quality about fever and other illnesses as Charles Dickens and Leo Tolstoy indicate:

'Have you a pain, mother?'

'There's a pain somewhere in the room, but I cannot be certain that I have got it.' Charles Dickens (1854)

Tossing to and fro upon his hot, uneasy bed; tormented by a fierce thirst nothing could appease; unable to find, in any change of posture, a moment's peace or ease; and rambling ever through deserts of thought where there was no resting-place . . . with no change but the restless shiftings of his body and the weary wanderings of his mind, constant still to one ever-present anxiety . . . always shadowy and dim, but recognizable for the same phantom in every shape it took, darkening every vision like an evil conscience, and making slumber horrible; in these slow tortures of his dread disease, the unfortunate Richard lay wasting and consuming inch by inch, until at last, when he seemed to fight and struggle to rise up, and to be held down by devils, he sunk into a deep sleep and dreamed no more. Charles Dickens (1840)

He felt that his agony was due both to his being thrust into that black hole and, still more, to his not being able to get right into it. What hindered him from getting into it was his claim that his life had been good. That very justification of his life held him fast and prevented him from advancing, and caused him more agony than everything else. Leo Tolstoy (1960)

I am poured out like water, and all my bones are out of joint; my heart is like wax; it is melted in the midst of my bowels. Psalms, xxii, 14

A new reality opens up:

It is in illness that we realize that we do not live alone, but are chained to a being of a different kingdom, from which abysses separate us, which does not know us and by which it is impossible to make ourselves understood: our body. Marcel Proust (1995)

Disease makes men more physical, it leaves them nothing but body. Thomas Mann (1996)

This pull into our bodies is a pull downwards. Illness humbles us and takes away our accustomed composure:

An accident or illness forces us to turn our attention to matters of the body and issues of the soul ... We are forced to seek healing, which begins with stopping ... and submitting to forces below us. Michael Meade (1993)

> My burning flesh in sweat did boil,
> My aching head did break;
> From side to side for ease I toil,
> So faint I could not speak.
> Anne Bradstreet (1969)

Illness seems to come between consciousness and the physical world like a malevolent persecutor. It comes between our intentions and our abilities, between our hopes and their fulfilment, and between naïvety and wisdom – which means that illness takes us into the realm of the soul.

Neglect of the Soul

Mankind's eternal cry is for release and the physician must answer it with something more than a test tube. C. Jeff Miller

To say that, for example, a man is made up of certain chemical elements is a satisfactory description only for those who intend to use him as a fertilizer. Herbert J. Muller (1943)

> It is difficult
> to get the news from poems
> yet men die miserably every day
> for lack
> of what is found there.
> William Carlos Williams (1951)

The situation which I believe we are all facing in the world today [is] one which the primitive world, the past life of Africa, knew only too well. It is a loss of first spirit, or to put it in the old-fashioned way, a loss of soul . . . the Zulu prophet . . . regarded this as the greatest calamity that could come to human beings. Indeed, the primitive world . . . designed elaborate ritual, ceaselessly fashioned myths, legends, stories and music to contain the meaning and feed the fire of the creative soul. Sir Laurens van der Post (1965)

Soul qualities tend to be undervalued in modern culture. In modern medical treatment the soul has an uneasy place:

> Gently swinging on its trapeze
> this grotesque limb, multiply skewered
> splintered bone and cobbled flesh
> announces to the world
> a feat of engineering.
>
> But faced with my hot human tears
> he backs off, out of his depth
> like a scolded cat who presents
> to his angry mistress
> a wounded bird.

Not until spring next year when
shiny skin blooms, healed bones
bear weight, muscles grow strong
and veins regenerate
will I believe, for the first time
in the surgeon's stupendous skill
and my body be mine again.

Cicely Herbert (1992)

One unintended outcome of the modern transformation of the medical care system is that it does just about everything to drive the practitioner's attention away from the experience of illness [thus missing what is] most ancient, most powerful, and most existentially rewarding. Arthur Kleinman (1988)

We lose a great deal by letting this aspect of caring decline:

Whenever treatment directly neglects the experience as such and hastens to reduce or overcome it, something is being done against the soul. For experience is the soul's one and only nourishment. James Hillman (1964)

Restoring Soul to its Rightful Place

My soul is a hidden orchestra; I know not what instruments, what fiddle strings and harps, drums and tambours I sound and clash inside myself. All I hear is the symphony. Fernando Pessoa (1991)

What is soul? It is hard to define. It is a certain way of being and perceiving. It requires going within. Soul involves being directly in touch with the experience of being alive, and a rich reflection on our experience, and it involves giving experience meaning. Soul means relating to images, art, literature and to other people's experience.

First, *soul* refers to the deepening of events into experiences; second the significance *soul* makes possible, whether in love or in religious concern, derives from its special *relation with death*. And third, by *soul* I mean the imaginative possibility in our natures, the experiencing through reflective speculation, dream, image, and *fantasy* – that mode

which recognizes all realities as primarily symbolic or metaphorical.
James Hillman (1975)

The soul of medicine is not to be found in test results or body scans, but in the soul of the patient, in the patient's subjective experience.

The man of Science seeks truth as a remote and unknown benefactor; he cherishes and loves it in his solitude: the Poet, singing a song in which all human beings join with him, rejoices in the presence of truth as our visible friend and hourly companion. Poetry is the breath and finer spirit of all knowledge: It is the impassioned expression which is in the countenance of all Science. William Wordsworth (1802)

I have the conviction that when physiology will be far enough advanced, the poet, the philosopher, and the physiologist will all understand each other. Claude Bernard (1927); medical researcher and contemporary of Louis Pasteur

> Enough of science and of art;
> Close up these barren leaves;
> Come forth and bring with you a heart
> That watches and receives.
> William Wordsworth (1802)

In fact, one of the effects of illness is to activate soul. It either gives us an opportunity to embrace soul, or it forces soulfulness upon us.

Humbled by Illness

A human being who is first of all an invalid is all body; therein lies his inhumanity and his debasement. Thomas Mann (1996)

The real problem is the shock of severe, dangerous illness, its unexpectedness and surprise. Most of us, patients and doctors alike, can ride almost all the way through life with no experience of real peril, and when it does come, it seems an outrage, a piece of unfairness . . . Lewis Thomas (1992)

I remained seriously ill for many months, inert, unnoticing, one of life's bad debts, more or less abandoned by all. 'You never moved or cried,' said my Mother. 'You just lay where I put you, like a little image, staring up at the ceiling all day.' In that motionless swoon I was but a clod, a scarce-breathing parcel of flesh. For a year I lay prone to successive invasions, enough to mop up an orphanage – I had diphtheria, whooping-cough, pleurisy, double pneumonia, and congestion of the bleeding lungs. My Mother watched, but could not help me; waited but could not hope. In those days young children dropped dead like chickens, their diseases not well understood; families were large as though by compensation; at least a quarter were not expected to survive. My father had buried three of his children already, and was quite prepared to do the same by me. Laurie Lee (1962)

Illness slows us down, erodes the dominance of intellect, and goes against our will. It makes us surrender; it makes us powerless, vulnerable and dependent. It makes us lose control, seek help in new directions, even ones previously rejected. It detaches us from life and makes us see it in a new way. It frightens us, puts us in our place and subdues our striving.

There is something in sickness that breaks down the pride of manhood. Washington Irving (1819–20)

I shall ask my swollen fingers permission to write a few words to you; I find they do not agree; perhaps they will in an hour or two. Mme de Sévigné

Medicine is concerned with the problem of keeping you alive; but serious illness asks the question for you 'What is life for?' Arthur Kleinman (1988)

For John Donne being ill brings forebodings of death:

. . . a fever can bring that head which yesterday carried a crown of gold . . . as low as his own foot today . . . A sick bed is a grave; and all that a patient says there is but a varying of his own epitaph. John Donne (1987)

In the same instant that I feel the first attempt of the disease, I feel its victory: in the twinkling of an eye, I can scarce see; instantly the taste is insipid, and fatuous; instantly the appetite is dull and desireless; instantly the knees are sinking and strengthless; and in an instant, sleep, which is the picture, the copy of death, is taken away, that the original, death itself, may succeed . . . John Donne (1987)

Illness can induce an identity crisis:

You perhaps have never been deeply and chronically ill; you perhaps do not know from within how sickness humbles – how it clouds and corrodes and befouls the sense of self. I do not know why this should be so, that physical disease plays such cruel vanquishing tricks upon the ego, even the sturdiest ego, given enough time . . . this is what the failures of the body do unerringly to the soul. Martha Weinman Lear (1980)

Here illness throws the sufferer into a new reality:

What was it like to be told I had cancer? The future disappeared. Loved ones became faces I would never see again. I felt I was walking through a nightmare that was unreal but utterly real. Arthur Frank (1991)

> Once could the Morn's first beams, the healthful breeze,
> All Nature charm, and gay was every hour; –
> But ah! not music's self, nor fragrant bower
> Can glad the trembling sense of wan Disease.
> Now that the frequent pangs my frame assail,
> Now that my sleepless eyes are sunk and dim,
> And seas of pain seem waving through each limb –
> Ah what can all life's gilded scenes avail?
>
> S. T. Coleridge (1969)

Relating to the Experience of Illness is the Soul Work of Medicine

In Tolstoy's portrayal of a terrible illness in a short story, Ivan Ilyich's sense of himself becomes so 'clouded and corroded and befouled' that he begins to argue with God and doubt the validity of his whole life. He is forced to seek his own soul, and ask for help:

He . . . restrained himself no longer but wept like a child. He wept at his own helplessness, at his terrible loneliness, at the cruelty of man, the cruelty of God, at the absence of God.

'Why hast Thou done this? Why hast Thou brought me to this? Why, why dost Thou torture me so dreadfully?'

He did not expect any answer, and yet wept because there was no answer and could be none. The pain flared up more acutely again but he did not stir and did not call. He said to himself: 'Go on, smite me! But why? What have I done to Thee? What is it for?'

Then he was still and not only ceased weeping but even held his breath and became all attention. He listened, as it were, not to an audible voice but to the voice of his soul, to the tide of his thoughts that rose up within him.

'What is it you want?' was the first clear conception capable of expression in words that he heard. 'What is it you want? What is it you want?' he repeated to himself.

'What do I want? Not to suffer. To live,' he answered.

And again he listened with such concentrated attention that even his pain did not distract him.

'To live. Live how?' asked his inner voice.

'Why, to live as I used to live – well and pleasantly.'

'As you used to live – well and pleasantly?' queried the voice. And he began going over in his imagination the best moments of his pleasant life. But oddly enough none of those best moments of his pleasant life now seemed at all what they had seemed at the time – none of them except his earliest memories of childhood. There, in childhood, there had been something really pleasant with which it would be possible to live if it could return. But the person who had experienced that happiness was no more: it was like a memory of someone else. Leo Tolstoy (1960)

When illness reaches this degree of severity it begins to control us and force us to reconsider our lives.

Illness is the doctor to whom we pay most heed: to kindness, to knowledge we make promises only: pain we obey. Marcel Proust (1995)

Illness and injuries can change us permanently:

Strangely enough, it was not illness, but the accident, which I believe most profoundly marked me. That blow in the night, which gave me concussion, scarred me, I think, for ever – put a stain of darkness upon my brow and opened a sinister door in my brain, a door through which I am regularly visited by messengers whose words just escape me, by glimpses of worlds I can never quite grasp, by grief, exultation, and panic . . . Laurie Lee (1962)

3

The Patient

They are and suffer; that is all they do . . .
W. H. Auden (1967)

The Isolation of the Sick

Illness of any duration brings abandonment and loneliness:

As sickness is the greatest misery, so the greatest misery of sickness
is solitude; when the infectiousness of the disease deters them who
should assist from coming; even the physician dares scarce come.
Solitude is a torment which is not threatened in hell itself . . . A long
sickness will weary friends at last, but a pestilential sickness averts
them from the beginning . . . this makes an infectious bed equal, nay
worse, than a grave. John Donne (1967)

Since sickness has an immobilizing, isolating and depressing effect, becoming
ill means joining a group of people who cannot make contact with each other:

They are and suffer; that is all they do;
A bandage hides the place where each is living,
His knowledge of the world restricted to
The treatment that the instruments are giving.

And lie apart like epochs from each other
– Truth in their sense is how much they can bear;
It is not talk like ours, but groans they smother –
And are remote as plants; we stand elsewhere.
W. H. Auden (1967)

The isolation can be self-imposed, perhaps because of guilt about being ill. It is possible to break out of this:

Isolation is one of the great weapons of the self-hater. Breaking silence releases us. When others know the worst about us, and accept us, we can believe we are truly valued. Starhawk (1987)

The Privileges of the Sick

The invalid's room had an atmosphere of peace and encouragement which affected all who entered it. Elizabeth Gaskell (1853)

This withdrawal from life has another side. It can be a special experience of protection and nurturing marked by ritual procedures and comforts, such as having one's bed made comfortable and pillows shaken out:

A pretty severe fit of indisposition which, under the name of a nervous fever, has made a prisoner of me for some weeks past, and is but slowly leaving me, has reduced me to an incapacity to reflect upon any topic foreign to itself. Expect no healthy conclusions from me this month, reader; I can offer you only sick men's dreams.

And truly the whole state of sickness is such; for what else is it but a magnificent dream for a man to lie a-bed, and draw daylight curtains about him; and, shutting out the sun, to induce a total oblivion of all the works which are going on under it? To become insensible to all the operations of life, except the beatings of one feeble pulse?

If there be a regal solitude, it is a sickbed. How the patient lords it there; what caprices he acts without control! how king-like he sways his pillow – tumbling, and tossing and shifting, and lowering, and thumping, and flattening, and moulding it, to the ever-varying requisitions of his throbbing temples.

He changes *sides* oftener than a politician. Now he lies full length, then half-length, obliquely, transversely, head and feet quite across the bed; and now one accuses him of tergiversation.

. . . How sickness enlarges a man's self to himself; he is his own exclusive object. Supreme selfishness is inculcated upon him as his only duty . . . he has nothing to think of but how to get well. Charles Lamb (1898)

In the following passage a child feels this elevated status of the sick most exquisitely:

So I grew to be, not a pale wasting boy, but sickly in another way, switching regularly from swaggering plumpness – a tough equality with other boys – to a monotonous return of grey-ghosted illness, hot and cold, ugly-featured and savage. When I was well I could hold my own; no one spared me because I didn't look delicate. But when I was ill, I just disappeared from the scene and remained out of sight for weeks. If it was summer when the fever caught me, I lay and sweated in my usual bed, never quite sure which of us was ill, me or the steaming weather. But in winter a fire was lit in the bedroom, and then I knew I was ill indeed. Wash-basins could freeze, icicles hang from the ornaments, our bedrooms remained normally unheated; but the lighting of a fire, especially in Mother's room, meant that serious illness had come. Laurie Lee (1962)

He starts to take advantage of this privileged position:

I remained in Mother's bedroom for many weeks, and a wood-fire burned all day. School friends, as though on a pilgrimage, came in their best clothes to bring me flowers. Girls sent me hens' eggs pencilled with kisses; boys brought me their broken toys. Even my schoolteacher (whose heart was of stone) brought me a bagful of sweets and nuts. Finally Jack, unable to keep the secret any longer, told me I'd been prayed for in church, just before collections, twice, on successive Sundays. My cup was full, I felt immortal; very few had survived that honour.

This time my convalescence was even more indulgent. I lived on Bovril and dry sponge cakes. I was daily embalmed with camphorated oils and hot-poulticed with Thermogene. Lying swathed in these pungent and peppery vapours, I played through my hours and days, my bed piled high with beads and comics, pressed flowers, old cartridges, jack-knives, sparking plugs, locusts, and several stuffed linnets.

I took every advantage of my spoiled condition and acted simple when things got tough. Particularly when it came to taking my medicine, a hell-draught of unspeakable vileness.

It was my sisters' job to get this down, and they would woo me with outstretched spoon.

'Now come on, laddie – One! Two! Three! . . .'

'You can clean out the jam pot after . . .'

'We'll peg up your nose. You won't taste it at all.'

I crossed my eyes and looked vacant.

'Be a good boy. Just this once. Come on.'

'Archie says No,' I said.

'What?'

'Archie,' I said, 'does not want the dose. Archie does not like the dose. And Archie will not have the dose. Says Archie.'

'Who's Archie?' they whispered, shaking their heads at each other. They usually left me then. Laurie Lee (1962)

I suddenly noticed that, although the tears were still falling down, the pain had disappeared. My conscience told me to stop but in order to be interesting a little bit longer I went on with my lamentations. However, this made me feel such a rogue that I was miserable over it all the rest of the day. Albert Schweitzer (1949)

The Tyranny of the Sick

Illness offers him a double advantage:
To escape from himself – and get the better of his wife.
T. S. Eliot (1949)

Be sicker yet, if sickness made
The world so marvellous kind.
Elizabeth Barrett Browning (1856)

Illness can be a source of power, an addiction, and a destructive source of satisfaction:

At the age of eight, I had no difficulty imagining heaven. Eternal bliss, with its absence of fear or conflict or roughness, would be merely a prolonged equivalent of how I felt after an asthma spasm had died down, relieved and easy, but a little bored too. The challenges of watchfulness and patience, the ferocious chest-stabbings and thumpings which could sometimes be parried by changing one's thoughts or the emphasis of one's breathing or one's position in bed – all this was living at its most intense. Non-asthmatic existence seemed a tepid business by comparison, with modest rewards and penalties.

To be accredited as an asthmatic was to become entitled to a life of seclusion and privilege. When I told my parents how soon I hoped to be up and about again, it was a polite hypocrisy, much as a millionaire behind the smoked windows of his limousine may say how he envies the poor and would like to share their simple pleasures. And always in their eyes the fear that I might die on them – the fear that was both the ultimate source of my power, yet was also irritating to me. Ferdinand Mount (1992)

Then Mother would come carolling upstairs with my breakfast, bright as a wind-blown lark.

'I've boiled you an egg and made you a nice cup of cocoa. And cut you some lovely thin bread and butter.'

The fresh boiled egg tasted of sun-warmed manna, the cocoa frothed and steamed, and the bread and butter – cut invalid fashion – was so thin you could see the plate through it. I gobbled it down, looking weak and sorry, while Mother straightened the bed, gave me my pencil and drawing-book, my beads and toys, and chatted of treats to come.

'I'm going to walk into Stroud and buy you a paintbox. And maybe some liquorice allsorts. All kinds of people have been asking after you. Even Miss Cohen! – just fancy that.'

Mother sat on the bed and looked at me proudly. All was love; and I could do no wrong. When I got up I would not have to chop any firewood, and nobody would be cross for a month. Oh, the fatal weakness that engaged me then, to be always and forever ill . . . Laurie Lee (1962)

And here the young patient goes into delusions of grandeur:

As soon as I recognized the returning face of my sickness – my hands light as feathers, a swaying in the head, and lungs full of pulsing thorns – the first thing I did was to recall my delusions and send messages to the anxious world. As I woke to the fever I thought of my subjects, and their concern always gave me comfort. Signals in Morse, tapped out on the bed rail, conveyed brief and austere intelligences. 'He is ill.' (I imagined the first alarm.) 'He has told his Mother.' (Some relief.) 'He is fighting hard.' (Massed prayers in the churches.) 'He is worse.' (Cries of doom in the streets.) There were times when I was almost moved to tears at the thought of my anxious people, the invisible multitudes up and down the land joined in grief at this threat to their King. How piteously they awaited each sombre bulletin, and how brave I was meanwhile. Certainly I took pains to give them something to be anxious about, but I also bid them be strong. 'He wishes no special arrangements made. Only bands and tanks. A parade of two. And perhaps a three minutes' silence.' Laurie Lee (1962)

> Flashed through the land the electric message came:
> He is not better, he is much the same.
> Anon

The Patient's Need to Articulate the Suffering

In illness we do not always express what is troubling us most:

Being ill is a peculiarly private experience, and most of the people I know who have gone through something serious tend to be reserved about it, changing the subject when it comes up . . . Lewis Thomas (1992)

Ill persons have a great deal to say for themselves, but rarely do I hear them talk about their hopes and fears, about what it is like to be in pain, about what sense they make of suffering and the prospect of death. Arthur Frank (1991)

Many fears may arise in illness; ultimately there is fear of death:

> I that in hale was and gladness
> Am troubled now with great sickness
> And feebled with infirmity:
> *Timor mortis conturbat me.*
>
> Our presence here is all vain glory,
> This false world is but transitory,
> The flesh is brittle, the Fiend is sly:
> *Timor mortis conturbat me.*

The state of man does change and vary,
Now sound, now sick, now blithe, now sorry,
Now dancing merry, now like to die.
Timor mortis conturbat me.
William Dunbar (1979)

The patient will need to find a way of expressing the symptoms and the fear:

Pain is a private experience, so is nausea, so are hunger and thirst. There are public *signs* of these states – groans, frowns, writhings, and so forth – but the actual pain and hunger and thirst are locked up in the unfortunate sufferer. The person with jaundice has only to exhibit it; someone with pain has to announce it. Jonathan Miller (1978)

A few patients may go to extremes in making the illness very public:

Dramatizing my condition seemed the next best thing to curing it. John Updike (1989)

Pneumonia was the thing I was best known for, and I made a big drama out of it. But it was not by any means my only weapon; I collected minor diseases also, including, in the space of a few short years, bouts of shingles, chickenpox, mumps, measles, ringworm, adenoids, scarlet fever, and catarrhal deafness. Laurie Lee (1962)

The Diagnostician Attends the Patient

After telling the story of looking after a little girl who was horribly burnt a doctor wrote:

She taught me a grand lesson in patient care: that it is possible to talk with patients, even those who are most distressed, about the actual experience of illness, and that witnessing and helping to order that experience can be of therapeutic value. Arthur Kleinman (1988)

Other patients teach their doctors 'about the difference between the patient's experience of illness and the doctor's attention to disease'. The next passage describes how the doctor gives attention to the disease.

In fact, a lot can be learnt about a pain from the way in which the patient points to it. Apart from saying something about where it is, the movement of the hand is often a tell-tale sign of its quality: if someone has angina, he often presses the front of his chest with a clenched fist; the whole fist shows that the pain is widespread; the fact that the fist is clenched tells us the pain has a gripping quality. The pain from peptic ulcer is often closely localized, and the patient usually tells you by delicately pointing to it with the tip of his index finger. When a stone lodges in the outlet to the kidney, the pain, as we have seen, tends to radiate in a long oblique line from the loin to the groin. Even if the patient doesn't describe this movement in words, he will sometimes do so by holding his side with the thumb at the back and the fingers pointing down at the front. If a pain is more or less superficial – what would normally be called soreness – the patient may lightly brush the skin with the outstretched tips of all five fingers. This sometimes happens in the early stages of shingles. The skilled physician can learn a lot from the pantomime of complaint. Jonathan Miller (1978)

This can go further; the healer can also develop a poetic sensibility; listening to the patient becomes a meeting of souls:

The physician enjoys a wonderful opportunity actually to witness the words being born. Their actual colours and shapes are laid before him carrying their tiny burdens which he is privileged to take into his care with their unspoiled newness. He may see the difficulty with which they have been born and what they are destined to do. No one else is present but the speaker and ourselves, we have been the words' very parents. Nothing is more moving. William Carlos Williams (1984)

The Patient and the Healer Share the Meaning

I kissed goodbye the howling beast on the borderline that separated
   you from me.
You'll never know the hurt I suffered nor the pain I rise above,
And I'll never know the same about you, your holiness or your
   kind of love,
And it makes me feel so sorry.
Bob Dylan (1974, 1975)

Ultimately there can be a communion where the meaning of life is shared between patient and healer. The patient reveals the core of his or her life, and the healer is thus touched by a sense of the drama of all life:

But after we have run the gamut of the simple meanings that come to one over the years a change gradually occurs. We have grown used to the range of communication which is likely to reach us. The girl who comes to me breathless, staggering into my office in her underwear, in her arms a still breathing infant, asking me to lock her mother out of the room; the man whose mind is gone – all of them finally say the same thing. And then a new meaning begins to intervene. For under that language to which we have been listening all our lives a new, more profound language underlying all the dialectics offers itself. It is what they call poetry. That is the final phase.

. . . beyond all they have been saying is what they have been trying to say . . . We begin to see that the underlying meaning of all they want to tell us and have always failed to communicate is the poem, the poem which their lives are being lived to realize. No one will believe it. And it is the actual words as we hear them spoken under all circumstances, which contain it . . . It is that essence which is hidden in the very words which are going in at our ears and from which we must recover underlying meaning as realistically as we recover metal out of ore.

. . . The poem springs from the half spoken words of such patients as the physician sees from day to day. He observes it in the peculiar, actual conformations in which its life is hid. Humbly he presents himself before it and by long practice he strives as best he can to interpret the manner of its speech. In that the secret lies. This, in the end, comes perhaps to be the occupation of the physician after a lifetime of careful listening. William Carlos Williams (1984)

These passages go beyond illness into the human life of which it is part. The result is a meeting of souls between patient and healer. This meeting is a kind of healing which gives inner strength and reminds us of what life is all about. It gives us a perspective on human suffering which embraces the whole meaning of a person's life. This perspective can only be called religious or spiritual, and is the breath of life for the soul.

4

The Ravages of Disease

Now death his servant sickness forth hath sent.
Francis Rous (1623)

Dim lamps with sickly rays scarce seem to glow;
Sighs heave in mournful moans, and tears o'erflow.
Sir Samuel Garth (1699)

> I saw him steal the light away
> That haunted in her eye:
> It went so gently none could say
> More than that it was there one day
> And missing by-and-by.
>
> I watched her long, and he stole
> Her lily tincts and rose;
> All her young spriteliness of soul
> Next fell beneath his cold control,
> And disappeared like those.
> Thomas Hardy (1960)

Facing the Truth

Our reactions to the symptoms of illness vary:

The attention that is given to them, however, and the actions to which they give rise depend on the person to whom they are happening. A large, unsightly lump may pass unnoticed by one person, while a

34

small swelling can cause great alarm in someone else; a pain which is played down by one person can cause another to cry out; a vain man with a well lit mirror will often recognize the first tinge of jaundice, whilst a more complacent person might have to turn bright yellow before he became aware of a colour change. Some people are simply more stoical. People who have been trained to look out for abnormal signs – such as medical students – tend to be hypochondriacal. Fear also plays an important part both in alerting and in blinding people to the possibility of illness: someone who is over-anxious about his health tends either to recognize signs and symptoms which his neighbour would overlook altogether, or to avoid examining himself for fear of finding out the worst. Jonathan Miller (1978)

Sometimes it is simply impossible to face the horror:

From the stump of the arm, the amputated hand,
I undo the clotted lint, remove the slough, wash off the matter
   and blood,
Back on his pillow the soldier bends with curv'd neck and
   side-falling head,
His eyes are closed, his face is pale, he dares not look on the
   bloody stump,
And has not yet look'd on it.
Walt Whitman (1865)

    I am their slowcoach colleague, half afraid,
    incurious. As a boy it was so: you know how
    my small hand never teased to pieces
    an alarm clock or flensed a perished mouse.
    And this larger hand's the same. It stretches now
    out from a white sleeve to hold up, mother,
    your x-ray to the glowing screen. My eyes look
    but don't want to; I still don't want to know.
    Dannie Abse (1989)

Realizing the Worst

Sweet Christ, rejoice in my infirmity;
There's little left I care to call my own.
Today they drained the fluid from a knee
And pumped a shoulder full of cortisone;
Thus I conform to my divinity
By dying inward, like an ageing tree.
Theodore Roethke (1986)

But months with a plastic bracelet . . . on a wrist growing daily bonier
and thinner, as the pain grew more intense and the nurses more jaunty
and the doctors, when one saw them, more officious; while her lovely
clothes hung in the wardrobe unworn, and her few friends gradually
failed to keep up their regular visits; while her pretty house accumu-
lated dust and damp and she stared and stared at the blank hospital
walls, unable, eventually, to read, to pray, even to think because of
the pain, and the ignominy of incontinence and bed sores . . . A. N.
Wilson (1982)

When the pain or other symptoms cannot be ignored, or when we are
given a diagnosis of a serious illness, then illness takes us one step further on
its journey:

There was no deceiving himself: something terrible, new and significant, more significant than anything that had ever happened in his
life, was taking place within him of which he alone was aware. Those
about him did not understand, or refused to understand, and believed
that everything in the world was going on as usual. This thought
tormented Ivan Ilyich more than anything. Leo Tolstoy (1960)

If only misery could be weighed,
And all my ills be put on scales!
But they outweigh the sands of the seas;
What wonder then if all my words are wild?
Job vi, 2–3

I am troubled;
I am bowed down greatly;
I go mourning all the day long.
For my loins are filled with a loathsome disease:
And there is no soundness in my flesh.

Psalm xxxviii, 6–7

The Evil Invasion

Sickness comes on horseback and departs on foot. Dutch proverb

The complaint at first seems like an invader, not really part of oneself. There is:

. . . the sense of another presence occupying your body and singling you out from the happy herds of healthy normal mankind. John Updike (1989)

Continuing and gaining in power the illness can take on its own malign existence:

It must therefore have been some seventeen or eighteen seconds after the starting gun that the first clutching came at my throat and I heard the first hollowed rasp within my chest, the one which sounds imported, seems almost to belong to someone else or to come from some source other than a human body. That primitive imagery of disease as an invader, an alien, is apt at this first onrush of symptoms; resentment, defiance, the defender's cunning are mobilized. But then the intrusive gremlin becomes a familiar, a known quantity, still resented but less keenly so. A kind of surly collaboration takes place, a wheezing accommodation, but always with a view to getting rid of him in the end, taking him by surprise perhaps or boring him into going away. Ferdinand Mount (1992)

The illness becomes 'it', a companion constantly submitting progress reports such as 'It's better today', or 'It's really getting me down.' Here is Tolstoy's character, Ivan Ilyich, trying to cope with his 'It', an unknown fatal disease, as it begins to haunt him:

It would come and stand before him and look at him and he would find himself rigid with fear and the light would die out of his eyes, and he would begin asking himself again whether It alone was true.

And his colleagues and subordinates would notice with surprise and distress that he . . . was getting confused and making mistakes . . .

He would go to his study, lie down, and again be alone with *It* . . . Face to face with *It*. And nothing to be done with *It*. Only look and shudder. Leo Tolstoy (1960)

John Donne says that in illness we are fighting a losing battle, like a farmer battling against weeds and all the brute forces of nature:

How ruinous a farm hath man taken on in taking on himself? How ready is the house every day to fall down, and how is all the ground overspread with weeds, all the body with diseases? Where not only every turf but every stone bears weeds; not only every muscle of the flesh but every bone of the body hath some infirmity; every little flint upon the face of this soil hath some infectious weed, every tooth in our head such a pain as a constant man is afraid of and yet ashamed of that fear, of that sense of pain . . . there are propensities to disease in the body out of which, without any other disorder, diseases will grow, and so we are put to a continual labour upon this farm, to a continual study of the whole complexion and constitution of our body. John Donne (1987)

The Fear and the Horror

What are the great disasters that engender fear in our hearts? War, famine, earthquake – and perhaps disease is one of the closest and most constant threats. These passages describe illness when it becomes an overwhelming horror:

Hans Castorp suddenly stopped, rooted to the spot by a perfectly ghastly sound coming from a little distance off round a bend in the corridor. It was not a loud sound, but so distinctly horrible that Hans Castorp made a wry face and looked wide-eyed at his cousin. It was coughing, obviously, a man coughing; but coughing like to no other Hans Castorp had ever heard, and compared with which any other had been a magnificent and healthy manifestation of life: a coughing that had no conviction and gave no relief, that did not even come out in paroxysms, but was just a feeble, dreadful welling up of the juices of organic dissolution. Thomas Mann (1996)

In the next piece a poet describes the horrendous disintegration of the body brought about by the plague:

> And when the morbid effluence through the throat
> Had reached the lungs, and filled the faltering heart,
> Then all the powers of life were loosened; forth
> Crept the spent breath most fetid from the mouth.
> As streams the putrid carcass: every power
> Failed through the soul – the body – and alike
> Lay they liquescent at the gates of death
> While with these dread insufferable ills
> A restless anguish joined, companion close,
> And sighs comixt with groans; and hiccough deep,
> And keen convulsive twitching ceaseless urged,
> Day after day, o'er every tortured limb,
> The wearied wretch still wearying with assault.
> . . . Then, toward the last, the nostrils close collapsed;
> The nose acute; eyes hollow; temples scooped;
> Frigid the skin, retracted; o'er the mouth
> A ghastly grin; the shrivelled forehead tense;
> The limbs outstretched, for instant death prepared . . .
>
> Lucretius (1805)

AIDS is perhaps the modern plague:

We're all going to go crazy, living this epidemic every minute, while the rest of the world goes on out there, all around us, as if nothing is happening, going on with their own lives and not knowing what it's like, what we're going through. We're living through war, but where they're living it's peacetime, and we're all in the same country. Larry Kramer (1993)

Illness becomes a private incommunicable horror:

Once when he got up from the commode too weak to pull up his trousers, he dropped into a soft low chair and surveyed with horror his bare, enfeebled thighs with the muscles so sharply marked on them. Leo Tolstoy (1960)

Then, seated on a three-legged chair,
Takes off her artificial hair:
Now, picking out a crystal eye,
She wipes it clean, and lays it by.
Her eyebrows from a mouse's hide,
Stuck on with art on either side,
Pulls off with care, and first displays 'em,
Then in a play-book smoothly lays 'em.
Now dexterously her plumpers draws,
That serve to fill her hollow jaws.
Untwists a wire; and from her gums
A set of teeth completely comes.
Pulls out the rags contrived to prop
Her flabby dugs, and down they drop.
Proceeding on, the lovely goddess
Unlaces next her steel-ribbed bodice;
Which by the operator's skill,
Press down the lumps, the hollows fill.
Up goes her hand and off she slips
The bolsters that supply her hips.
With gentlest touch, she next explores
Her chancres, issues, running sores . . .
Jonathan Swift (1983)

Set Apart by Illness

I died and came to life again as a patient. Oscar Wilde (1962)
    If we are not well we are selected for membership of 'the fellowship
of those who bear the mark of pain'. Albert Schweitzer (1933)

Go to the sick man's bedside – mark how dim
The eye, once bright with meaning; and the limb
Once strung with nature's firmest energies,
See how unnerved and impotent it lies!
Where are the kindlings of the mighty soul,
Whose daring independence scorn'd control?

Where are the quick sensations, once alive
To all the rapture life can ever give?
Dead to delight, he loathing turns aside
From ev'ry luxury kindness can provide;
His aching temples throb with furious beat,
Flushed is his burning cheek with fev'rish heat;
To his parch'd mouth, his tongue, unmoistened, cleaves,
Refreshing sleep his wakeful eyelids leaves;
Or if a moment they may chance to close,
'Tis not to slumber in a calm repose,
But in distempered and delirious dreams,
Beset with foes and fears and death he seems,
Till waked with horror, he affrighted springs,
Glad to escape those dark imaginings.

Samuel Bartlett Parris (1829)

We are no longer in control of our lives and bodies:

One might imagine that somewhere there exists a grim power which amuses itself with mortals as they amuse themselves with fish. Some bait is temptingly played before your eyes. You seize it greedily. Then comes a wholly undreamt-of twinge, and you find a hook in your flesh, in the shape of a lung or heart disease. After allowing you more or less line, the unseen hand winds you up, and with an unceremonious knock on the head deposits you in its sombre creel. The first frenzied appeal on finding oneself, so to speak, 'hooked', is, of course, to the doctor, who, with a faith on the part of the public which must to him be quite touching, is called on and expected to perform a miracle – to enable overworked brain and stomach to continue to overwork themselves, and to restore and maintain health under conditions of disease. Christopher Home Douglas (1874)

A person now becomes a patient, and is labelled and dressed accordingly. He or she is given a new identity, a new dwelling place and a new role in society:

No longer a person in the ordinary world, he is not yet formally accepted by his fellow patients – anxious and isolated in his novice pyjamas, he awaits the formal act of aggregation. He is introduced to the ward sister, hands over his street clothes, submits to a questionnaire

by the houseman and registrar. Dressed with all the dignified credentials of a formally admitted patient, he awaits the forthcoming event.
Jonathan Miller (1978)

One's own clothes are replaced by an anonymous white nightgown, one's wrist is clasped by an identification bracelet with a number. One becomes subject to institutional rules and regulations. One is no longer a free agent; one no longer has rights; one is no longer in the world-at-large. It is strictly analogous to becoming a prisoner and humiliatingly reminiscent of one's first day at school. One is no longer a person, one is now an inmate. Oliver Sacks (1989)

We heave, we groan, mouth prayers and mantras
and fulminate at grievances that rankle.
We freeze, we sweat, we shake or shout,
bring weary footsteps hurrying to our sides
and swallow pride with pills and water.
Cicely Herbert (1992)

How Suffering is Ignored

In health we may choose to ignore illness and distance ourselves from people who are suffering — by simply neglecting to visit them or by rejecting them emotionally. Either way, the sick person's isolation increases:

About suffering they were never wrong,
The Old Masters: how well they understood
Its human position; how it takes place
While someone else is eating or opening a window or just walking
    dully along;
How, when the aged are reverently, passionately waiting
For the miraculous birth, there always must be
Children who did not specially want it to happen, skating
On a pond at the edge of the wood:
They never forgot
That even the dreadful martyrdom must run its course
Anyhow in a corner, some untidy spot

Where the dogs go on with their doggy life and the torturer's
    horse
Scratches its innocent behind on a tree.

In Brueghel's *Icarus*, for instance: how everything turns away
Quite leisurely from the disaster; the ploughman may
Have heard the splash, the forsaken cry,
But for him it was not an important failure; the sun shone
As it had to on the white legs disappearing into the green
Water; and the expensive delicate ship that must have seen
Something amazing, a boy falling out of the sky,
Had somewhere to get to and sailed calmly on.
W. H. Auden (1967)

At certain moments, after a prolonged bout of suffering, he craved
more than anything – ashamed as he would have been to own it – for
someone to feel sorry for him just as if he were a sick child. He
longed to be petted, kissed and wept over, as children are petted and
comforted. He knew he was an important functionary, that he had a
beard turning grey, and that therefore what he longed for was impossible; but nevertheless he longed for it. Leo Tolstoy (1960)

> 'Tis true – then why should I repine
> To see my life so fast decline?
> But why obscurely here alone,
> Where I am neither loved nor known?
> My state of health none care to learn;
> My life is here no soul's concern.
> And those with whom I now converse
> Without a tear will tend my hearse . . .
> Jonathan Swift (1983)

> He died alone; in all this mighty city
> Not one came forth to stand beside his bed,
> To speak of hope, to whisper words of pity,
> To close his weary lids when he was dead.
> John Chalmers Da Costa (1944)

I am – yet what I am, none cares or knows;
My friends forsake me like a memory lost:
I am the self-consumer of my woes . . .
John Clare (1979)

I view the crowds whom Youth and Health inspire,
Hear the loud laugh and catch the sportive lay,
Then sigh and think – I too could laugh and play
And gaily sported on the Muse's lyre,
Ere Tyrant Pain had chas'd away delight,
Ere the wild pulse throbb'd anguish thro' the night.
S. T. Coleridge (1969)

5

Sympathy

Sympathy for the Sick

He preaches patience that never knew pain. Proverb

Another man may be sick too, and sick to death and this affliction may lie in his bowels like gold in a mine and be of no use to him; but this bell that tells me of his affliction digs out and applies that gold to me, if by this consideration of another's danger I take mine own into contemplation. No man is an island, entire of itself; every man is a piece of the continent, a part of the main ... any man's death diminishes me because I am involved in mankind; and therefore never send to know for whom the bell tolls: it tolls for thee. John Donne (1987)

For the healthy, contact with the sick is an opportunity to give help and develop compassion:

I do not know when it was that I understood that it is precisely this hell in which we wage our lives that offers us the energy, the possibility to care for each other. A surgeon does not slip from his mother's womb with compassion smeared upon him like the drippings of his birth. It is much later that it comes ... between the sick man and the one who tends him there may spring that profound courtesy that the religious call love. Richard Selzer (1977)

Pity is the feeling which arrests the mind in the presence of whatsoever is grave and constant in human sufferings and unites it with the human sufferer. James Joyce (1995)

To moisten the sufferer's parched lips through the long night-watches, to bear up the drooping head, to lift the helpless limbs, to divine the want that can find no utterance beyond the feeble motion of the hand or beseeching glance of the eye – these are the offices that

demand no questionings, no casuistry, no assent to propositions, no weighing of consequences. Within the four walls where the stare and glare of the world are shut out, every voice is subdued – where a human being lies prostrate, thrown on the tender mercies of his fellow, the moral relation of man to man is reduced to its utmost clearness and simplicity . . . as we bend over the sickbed, all the forces of our nature rush towards channels of pity, of patience, and of love, and sweep down the miserable choking drift of our quarrels, our debates, our would-be wisdom and our clamorous selfish desires. This blessing of serene freedom from the importunities of opinion . . . is one source of that sweet calm which is often felt by the watcher in the sickroom . . .
George Eliot (1858)

We have probably all known those embarrassing moments of uncertainty on first entering a hospital ward:

> Awkward and hushed,
> Then try a smile
> Then shift and fidget, stood without dignity
> At the beck and call of junior nurse or maid,
> Hiding their flowers, helpless, almost afraid.
> Peter Dale (1976)

The Limits of Sympathy

A bore is one who, when you ask him how he is, tells you. Anon.

'How are you, Podge?' I said, as I sat down in a leather armchair beside him.

I only meant 'How do you do?' but he rolled his big eyes sideways at me in his flabby face (it was easier than moving his face) and he answered:

'I'm not as well as I was yesterday afternoon. Last week I was feeling pretty good part of the time, but yesterday about four o'clock the air turned humid, and I don't feel so well.' Stephen Leacock (1984)

There are limits to our inner supplies of sympathy, and limits too to the actual benefits it can achieve:

What a stupid thing
to go and do to yourself.
I'm telling you you're on your own.
Not a friend in the world.
You're a bloody nuisance Viv
always have been.

Don't think you're on holiday.
I've fed the cat
and if there's anything you want
– fags, knickers and that –
I'll get them for you
but you'll have to pay
it's not coming from my pocket Viv
no way.

I've only come to see you're all right
you silly old bugger.
Cicely Herbert (1992)

Nor do I in any way approve of the modern sympathy with invalids.
I consider it morbid. Illness of any kind is hardly a thing to be
encouraged in others. Oscar Wilde (1895)

I'd forever talk to you, but soon my words, they would turn into
  a meaningless ring,
For deep in my heart I know there is no help I can bring.
Everything passes, everything changes, just do what you think
  you should do.
And someday maybe, who knows, baby, I'll come and be cryin'
  to you.
Bob Dylan (1964a)

Receiving Comfort from Others

'Mongst all the arts that saving be
None so sublime as sympathy.
Thomas Flatman (1674)

The bitterness of suffering is sweetened by sympathy:

In the tendrils of their care
I leaf and learn again.
They wash me, change me, talk to me,
wipe away the spills and tears
clean pin-sites, understand
but do not pander to my pain.
Cicely Herbert (1992)

The patient may feel better knowing of others' suffering and feel less alone:
We are so fond of each other because our ailments are the same.
Jonathan Swift (1963)

But how many of us dare to confess what so many of us have felt, that the burden of their own grief seemed easier to bear while all women and men around us were in mourning, that the wound in their own flanks seemed almost to heal while the blood was flowing from so many other wounds? Who dared to grumble over his own fate while the fate of the world was at stake? Who dared to whimper over his own pain while all these mutilated men were lying on their stretchers silent with set teeth? Axel Munthe (1949)

Florence Nightingale warns against unrealistic cheerfulness when caring for the sick:

I really believe there is scarcely a greater worry which invalids have to endure than the incurable hopes of their friends . . . attempting to 'cheer' the sick by making light of their danger and by exaggerating their probabilities of recovery . . . The fact is that the patient is not 'cheered' at all by these well-meaning, most tiresome friends . . . He feels isolated in the midst of friends. He feels what a convenience it would be, if there were any single person to whom he could speak simply and openly, without pulling the string upon himself of this shower-bath of silly hopes and encouragements. Florence Nightingale (1860)

Visitors are no proper companions in the chamber of sickness. They come when I could sleep or read, they force me to attend when my mind calls for relaxation, and to speak when my powers will hardly actuate my tongue. Samuel Johnson (1952)

Many will disagree with this sentiment:

> Apt words have power to 'suage
> the tumours of a troubled mind,
> and are as balm to fester'd wounds.
>
> John Milton (1671)

Coping with It

'You and your toothache. But what's going on in the Mekong Delta? Have you read?'

'Yes . . . I've read. Bad. Very very bad. But I must admit that this ache, this draught that always hits the same nerve, this pain, which isn't even so bad, but which I can localize, and which never stirs from the spot, affects me, shakes me and lays me bare more than the photographed pain of this world, which for all its enormity is abstract because it doesn't hit my nerve.' Günter Grass (1970)

The narrator in the next passage refers to books like *The Magic Mountain*, a novel which, among other things, is about the nature of disease. He maintains that some people cannot or do not want to philosophize when they are ill:

We didn't have serious talks in the sanatorium. I have read those famous books in which patients with consumption talk about life and death and philosophy. We were not like that. That may be because we were young, but even the older patients, some of them mortally ill, seemed to exchange banal pleasantries most of the time. They had the sort of conversations you might have in a holiday hotel or on a cruise. Why should people be expected to talk about the meaning of life merely because they happen to be ill? That is just the time when there is no time to think about such things, because the body is so greedy for attention. Ferdinand Mount (1992)

There will be times when simply dealing with pain takes all our attention and courage, and we become heroes:

> In the fell clutch of circumstance
> I have not winced nor cried aloud.
> Under the bludgeoning of chance
> My head is bloody, but unbow'd.
>
> W. E. Henley (1992)

Sometimes it is best to keep quiet about one's troubles:

> Talk health. The dreary, never-ending tale
> Of mortal maladies is worn and stale;
> You cannot charm or interest or please
> By harping on that minor chord, disease.
> Say you are well or all is well with you,
> And God shall hear your words, and make them true.
>
> Ella Wheeler Wilcox (1921)

However, to be too proud, or habitually hide one's suffering, does not help:

> Words will avail the wretched mind to ease
> And much abate the dismal black disease.
>
> Horace

> Give sorrow words; the grief that does not speak
> Whispers the o'erfraught heart and bids it break.
>
> William Shakespeare, *Macbeth*, IV, iii, 209–10

> Nobody heard him, the dead man,
> But still he lay moaning:
> I was much farther out than you thought
> And not waving but drowning.

Poor chap, he always loved larking
And now he's dead
It must have been too cold for him, his heart gave way,
They said.

Oh, no no no, it was too cold always
(Still the dead one lay moaning)
I was much too far out all my life
And not waving but drowning.
Stevie Smith (1985)

Being Cheerful in Adversity

The human spirit can be cheerful even in the darkest times:

We sail in leaky bottoms and on great and perilous waters; and to take a cue from the dolorous old naval ballad, we have heard the mermaidens singing, and know that we shall never see dry land any more. Old and young, we are all on our last cruise. If there is a fill of tobacco among the crew, for God's sake pass it round, and let us have a pipe before we go! Robert Louis Stevenson (1885a)

If sadly thinking, with spirits sinking,
Could more than drinking my cares compose,
A cure for sorrow from sighs I'd borrow,
And hope tomorrow would end my woes.
But as in wailing there's nought availing,
And Death unfailing will strike the blow,
Then for that reason, and for a season,
Let us be merry before we go.
John Philpot Curran

6

Living with Illness

A man must give sicknesses their passage . . . Michel de Montaigne (1958)

The Diagnosis: Naming the Problem

To have a disease is to feel unclean, contaminated, defective. Marc Ian Barasch (1995)

One of the first things a sick person needs is a diagnosis. Then he or she is not so much a sick person as a person with a sickness – when this separation is made the person feels safer:

The illness, as an undefined force, is a potential threat to our very being . . . By fearing its threat we embrace it and make it specially our own. That is why patients are inordinately relieved when doctors give their complaint a name . . . They can now struggle or complain *against* it. To have a complaint recognized is to be made stronger. John Berger and Jean Mohr (1967)

But some diagnoses bring new problems:

I discovered my lump in October. As soon as I went to the doctor with it, I was sure that something big, something important was happening. I felt exactly as I had as a child when embarking on a roller-coaster ride; that long, slow, ominous, tugging pull up the hill before the first stomach-turning descent and all the subsequent peaks and valleys. Julie Friedberger (1996)

Fighting Illness

[Are] all the thoughts, pains, joys, of mortal breath
A war-embrace of wrestling life and death?
S. T. Coleridge (1969)

The fight is at times a desperate one:

People with other diseases are just plain sick; those with cancer 'fight' it. During my heart trouble, no one suggested I fight my heart, but one of the first things I was told about cancer was, 'You have to fight.' Read any set of obituaries. People die of cancer after a 'valiant battle' or a 'long bout'. Government research programmes are 'wars' on cancer. Newspaper stories that refer to poverty, crime, and drug abuse as 'cancers' reflect society's attitude toward cancer as the dreaded other. Against this other, combat is the only appropriate response. But I do not believe that illness should be lived as a fight.

We thought of ourselves as civilians whose home had become a battlefield. Demands and crises followed one after the other so fast that we felt buffeted. Arthur Frank (1991)

Doctors may feel it is necessary to:

. . . attack the disease with all the weapons one has . . . without a thought for the person who is ill. Oliver Sacks (1973)

A battle is also taking place within the patient:

It seemed to him that he and his pain were being thrust somewhere into a narrow, deep black sack, but though they kept forcing him farther and farther in they still could not push him to the bottom. And this horrible state of affairs was accompanied by agony. And he was frightened and yet wanted to fall into the sack, he struggled and at the same time cooperated. Leo Tolstoy (1960)

I fought with my twin,
That enemy within
'Til both of us fell by the way.
Horseplay and disease
Is killing me by degrees
While the law looks the other way.
Bob Dylan (1978)

The Patient as Victim

Here is the pessimistic view of humanity being persecuted on all sides by malevolent forces:

> . . . If man could see
> The perils and disease that he elbows,
> Each day he walks a mile; which catch at him,
> Which fall behind and graze him as he passes;
> Then would he know that life's a single pilgrim,
> Fighting unarmed against a thousand soldiers.
> Thomas Beddoes (1850)

There is scarce anything that hath not killed somebody. John Donne (1987)

He saw peril in everything, disaster was ever at hand. Some mayhem with our name on it lurked around the edges of our neighbourhood waiting for a lapse of parental oversight during which to spirit us away. In the most innocent of enterprises he saw a danger. In every football game he saw the ruptured spleen, death by drowning in every backyard pool, leukaemia in every bruise, broken necks on trampolines, the deadly pox or fever in every rash or bug bite. Thomas Lynch (1997)

Wild animals are in touch with their instincts and live united with nature, but we have lost the untamed vigour which preserves health:

Here we shrink in our proportion, sink in our dignity, in respect of very mean creatures, who are physicians to themselves. The hart that is pursued and wounded, they say, knows an herb which, being eaten, throws off the arrow: a strange kind of vomit. The dog that pursues it, though he be subject to sickness, even proverbially, knows his grass that recovers him . . . but the apothecary is not so near [man], nor the physician so near him, as they two are to other creatures; man hath not that innate instinct to apply those natural medicines to his present danger as those inferior creatures have. John Donne (1987)

So all our hard work to preserve health can be demolished at the whim of our persecutors:

We study health and we deliberate upon our meats, and drink, and air, and we hew and we polish every stone that goes to that building: and so our health is a long and a regular work: but in a minute a cannon batters all, overthrows all, demolishes all. John Donne (1987)

And all is pessimism:

O what a giant is man, when he fights against himself, and what a dwarf when he needs or exercises his own assistance for himself! John Donne (1987)

The syndrome known as life is too diffuse to admit of palliation. For every symptom that is eased, another is made worse. Samuel Beckett (1957)

Sources of Hope

But there is hope, because we are not defenceless victims of the environment. We must not forget that the human organism has its powers of regeneration:

It is a distortion to picture the human being as a teetering, fallible contraption, always needing watching and patching, always on the verge of flapping to pieces; this is the doctrine that people hear most often, and most eloquently, on all our information media . . . The great secret of medicine, known to doctors but still hidden from the public, is that most things get better by themselves. Lewis Thomas (1983)

But why is it so difficult to imagine that I am cared about, that something takes an interest in what I do, that I am perhaps protected, maybe even kept alive not altogether by my own will and doing? Why do I prefer insurance to the invisible guarantees of existence? For it sure is easy to die. A split second of inattention and the best-laid plans of a strong ego spill out on the sidewalk. Something saves me every day from falling down the stairs, tripping at the curb, being blindsided.

How is it possible to race down the highway, tapedeck singing, thoughts far away, and stay alive? What is this 'immune system' that watches over my days, my food sprinkled with viruses, toxins, bacteria? Even my eyebrows crawl with mites, like little birds on a rhino's back. We name what preserves us instinct, self-preservation, sixth sense, subliminal awareness (each of which, too, is invisible yet present). Once upon a time what took such good care of me was a guardian spirit, and I damn well knew how to pay it appropriate attention. James Hillman (1996)

In this paragraph John Donne admits there is hope in the form of physicians:

The disease hath established a kingdom, an empire in me, and will have certain *arcana imperii*, secrets of state by which it will proceed, and not be bound to declare them. But yet against those secret conspiracies of the state the magistrate hath the rack; and against these insensible diseases physicians have their examinations . . . John Donne (1987)

There is another approach to this which also brings some comfort. We cannot expect our bodies to last for ever. Some acceptance of the wear and tear of life will free us from anxiety:

People who are always taking care of their health are like misers, who are hoarding a treasure which they have never spirit enough to enjoy. Laurence Sterne (1780)

Use your health, even to the point of wearing it out. That is what it is for. Spend all you have before you die; and do not outlive yourself. George Bernard Shaw (1948)

It is better to lose health like a spendthrift than waste it like a miser. Robert Louis Stevenson (1881)

Waiting without Hope

What can't be cured were best endured. Seneca (1997)

There are times when hope is impossible:

> What's he, born to be sick, so always dying,
> That's guided by inevitable fate;
> That comes in weeping, and that goes out crying;

Whose calendar of woes is still in date;
Whose life's a bubble, and in length a span;
A concert still in discords? 'Tis a man.
William Browne (1616)

Then we have to learn to live without hope:

For a year I lay prone to successive invasions, enough to mop up an orphanage – I had diphtheria, whooping-cough, pleurisy, double pneumonia, and congestion of the bleeding lungs. My Mother watched, but could not help me; waited but could not hope. Laurie Lee (1962)

I said to my soul, be still, and wait without hope
For hope would be hope for the wrong thing: wait without love
For love would be love of the wrong thing; there is yet faith
But the faith and the love and the hope are all in the waiting.
T. S. Eliot (1944)

'Is there no hope?' the sick man said,
The silent doctor shook his head.
John Gay (1727)

Hope can become foolish hope:

In fiction, in our own heads and in our own hearts, we continually rewrite the human script. The engine finally coughs into life, the plane takes off, the hero is invulnerable to the bullets of the bad guy, and at the last moment a man in a white coat runs up the ward with a wonder drug. Kevin Toolis (1996)

Obsession with Health

The pursuit of health and fitness has become one of our Western addictions – we cannot accept our vulnerability and mortality:

As a people we have become obsessed with health ... there is something fundamentally, radically unhealthy about all this ... we have lost confidence in the human body. Lewis Thomas (1980)

Ours is an age which consciously pursues health, and yet only believes in the reality of sickness. Gian-Paolo Biasin (1975)

Painlessness is now among our national obsessions: anaesthesia has become, like television, a household god, and at the first sign of discomfort we rush for our pills and doctors ... The unexpected intrusion of pain, like an ingot hissing deep within the abdomen, seems almost a reminder of forgotten knowledge. David B. Morris (1980)

The question of what is normal and what is pathological is increasingly important:

Every society establishes a whole series of systems of oppositions – between good and evil, permitted and prohibited, lawful and illicit, criminal and non-criminal, etc. All these oppositions, which are constitutive of society, today in Europe are being reduced to the simple opposition between normal and pathological. This opposition not only is simpler than others, but also has the advantage of letting us believe there is a technique to bring the pathological back to normal. Michel Foucault

This striving for health is not necessarily good for us:

If you start to think about your physical or moral condition, you usually find that you are sick. J. W von Goethe

If you mean to keep as well as possible, the less you think about your health the better. Oliver Wendell Holmes (1891)

Real pain can alone cure us of imaginary ills. S. T. Coleridge (1895)

Nothing is more fatal to health than over care of it. Benjamin Franklin

Jogging is not always the answer:

He who pursues the peak of health pursues a fleeting phantom which cannot be overtaken in the running . . . Edelstein (1945)

Accepting the Experience of Illness

Those who are low need fear no fall. Proverb

When patients cannot be certain of recovery, they have to 'bow to some big thing' and in this way they achieve some dignity:

Spry, wry, and gray as these march sticks,
Percy bows, in his blue peajacket, among the narcissi.
He is recuperating from something on the lung.

The narcissi, too, are bowing to some big thing:
It rattles their stars on the green hill where Percy
Nurses the hardship of his stitches, and walks and walks.

There is a dignity to this; there is a formality –
The flowers vivid as bandages, and the man mending.
They bow and stand; they suffer such attacks!

And the octogenarian loves the little flocks.
He is quite blue; the terrible wind tries his breathing.
The narcissi look up like children, quickly and whitely.
Sylvia Plath (1985)

The best way of dealing with a minor illness is to sit back and accept it:
It is Tuesday, your twenty-fifth birthday. It is your lucky day. Everything good that has ever come your way has befallen you on Tuesday. So that when you awaken from sound sleep to find . . . what's this! . . . your head aching at the temples, your bones and joints stiff, your muscles sore, and a nose that pours and plashes as any freshet at monsoon, you are desolate. How can this be? . . .

Oft and again have I myself awakened to similar indisposition. Let me tell you what is the very best thing to do. Slide down a bit in the bed; take the edge of the sheet in the fingers of both hands and pull it up such that it conceals your face; now smile . . . Present your order for breakfast in bed (anorexia is not necessarily a symptom of the disease), and settle in for a day and a night of perfect happiness. Richard Selzer (1982)

Perhaps a Taoist acceptance is the best approach to all illnesses, if they depart more quickly that way:
A man must give sicknesses their passage; and I find that they stay least with me, because I allow them their swinge, and let them do what they list. And contrary to common received rules, I have without aid or art rid myself of some that are deemed the most obstinately

lingering and unremovably obstinate. Let nature work; let her have her will: she knoweth what she hath to do, and understands herself better than we do. But such a one died of it you will say; so shall you doubtless, if not of that, yet of some other disease . . . I have suffered rheums, gouty defluxions, relaxations, panting of the heart, and other suchlike accidents, to grow old in me, and die their natural deaths; all of which left me when I half enured and framed myself to foster them. They are better conjured by courtesy, than by bragging or threats. Michel de Montaigne (1958)

[Shaw] was a good patient because his mind was tranquil. His days lay mapped out ahead, and if illness or accident interrupted their ordered progress he would quietly withdraw from the world as animals do, and wait unperturbed until he got well again. This tranquillity of spirit was, I think, as responsible for his long life as what he had to eat and drink or what he refrained from eating and drinking. Blanche Patch (1951)

Such bouts of delirium were familiar visitations, and my family had long grown used to them. Jack would inquire if I needed to groan quite so much, while Tony examined me with sly speculation; but for the most part I was treated like a dog with distemper and left to mend in my own good time. The fevers were dramatic, sudden, and soaring, but they burnt themselves out very quickly. There would follow a period of easy convalescence, during which I lived on milk custards and rusks; then I'd begin to feel bored, I'd get up and go out, start a fight, and sickness was closed. Laurie Lee (1962)

There comes a period in most illnesses, I think, sometimes during a temporary respite, more often perhaps at the first dawn of convalescence, when one becomes extraordinarily conscious, yet without discomfort, of the almost trivial delicacy of one's surrounding tissue . . . yet I do suppose we forget it, most of us, and probably quite healthily, when once the dwelling is bricked up again, and the new paint is on, and it stands foursquare to winds that may not enter now. And yet again if the message has once been heard . . . I don't believe it is ever entirely lost. And there perhaps may lie the key to all the mystery; so that when the last storm blows, and Nature must shake her head, and let the frail house fall, its tenant may not go out altogether unprepared. Sir Henry Howard Bashford (1692)

7

Making Sense of Illness

All interest in disease and death is only another expression of interest in life. Thomas Mann (1996)

The Mystery of Illness

There are few things more confusing to people than the process of regaining or attaining health. It is one of the great mysteries. Alice Walker (1990)

While we are healthy we get on with our lives; while we are ill we are occupied with getting well again. We rarely ask why and how we move between these two states:

When my body suddenly revolts like a bucking horse – breaking out in hives, crumpling in a faint, or refusing the dinner I just ate – I am often shocked to realize it has a will of its own perfectly capable of supplanting my own. Sometimes I feel betrayed by this being I thought was my ally, and protest vehemently, like an ageing autocrat cornered in his office in the midst of a political coup: 'Why me? Why now? What's wrong? This isn't fair!' Kat Duff (1994)

Defining the Condition: The Origins of Illness

The beginning of health is to know disease. Miguel de Cervantes
Disease is the retribution of outraged Nature. Hosea Ballou
What is the source of disease and the sufferings it causes? What is it that

makes disease possible? What is the difference between a body where illness develops and one where it does not? This section attempts to shed light on the personal origins of disease.

> For what wears out the life of mortal men?
> 'Tis that from change to change their being rolls;
> 'Tis that repeated shocks, again, again,
> Exhaust the energy of strongest souls
> And numb the elastic powers.
> Till having us'd our nerves with bliss and teen,
> And tir'd upon a thousand schemes our wit,
> To the just-pausing Genius we remit
> Our worn-out life, and are – what we have been.
> Matthew Arnold (1853)

Doctors do not often think about illness. They think about particular diseases but rarely about the nature and essence of illness or disease. This is partly because the subject is extremely complex. At a metaphysical level, there is the whole question of the purpose of suffering; and there is the question of the meaning of the illness for the individual, its timing in relation to events in the person's life, and the consequences which might be expected to follow from having been ill. These issues are highly relevant for doctors wishing to look beyond the diseased organ, although they are not much favoured in orthodox medical circles, because psychological, social and even spiritual concepts are involved. Glin Bennet (1987)

Punishment from the Gods

In the Old Testament illness was the will of God:

But it shall come to pass, if thou wilt not harken to the voice of the Lord thy God, to observe to do all his commandments and his statutes which I command thee this day; that all these curses shall come upon thee, and overtake thee:

The lord shall smite thee with a consumption, and with a fever, and with an inflammation, and with an extreme burning, and with the sword, and with blasting, and with mildew; and they shall pursue thee until thou perish.

The lord will smite thee with the botch of Egypt, and with the emerods, and with the scab, and with the itch, whereof thou canst not be healed.

The Lord shall smite thee with madness, and blindness, and astonishment of the heart.

The lord shall smite thee in the knees, and in the legs, with a sore botch that cannot be healed, from the soul of thy foot unto the top of thy head.

And thou shalt become an astonishment, a proverb, and a byword, among all nations whither the Lord shall lead thee. Deuteronomy xxviii, 15, 22, 27–8, 35, 37

'Thus, a sickness . . . a sore place, if we may call it so, in your spirit hath immediately its appropriate manifestation in your bodily frame. Would you, therefore, that your physician heal the bodily evil? How may this be unless you first lay open to him the wound or trouble in your soul?'

'No, not to thee, not to an earthly physician!' cried Mr Dimmesdale, passionately, and turning his eyes, full and bright, and with a kind of fierceness . . . 'Not to thee, but if it be the soul's disease, then do I commit myself to the one Physician of the soul.' Nathaniel Hawthorne (1850)

In indigenous cultures the cause of illness was invasion by evil spirits. We used to fear gods or demons; now we fear bacteria and viruses, which are perhaps demons in another form:

> Sinners in the old regime
> Had worse to fear than homilies:
> Demons lashed them with disease
> And hell was not an idle dream.
>
> Now those demons have been tamed –
> Not exorcized by priest or pope,
> But sighted through the microscope,
> Preserved, and classified, and named.
> Edward Lowbury (1968)

Invasion by Enemies: Bacteria and Viruses

Next, take the question of germs and bacilli. Don't be scared of them. That's all. That's the whole thing, and if you once get on to that you need never worry again.

If you see a bacilli, walk right up to it and look it in the eye. If one flies into your room, strike it with a hat or with your towel . . . It will soon get sick of that. Stephen Leacock (1939)

Does disease originate solely 'out there in the world' or does the host organism, perhaps via an unhealthy immune system, allow it to develop? This argument began as soon as Pasteur discovered bacteria:

Illnesses hover constantly about us, their seeds blown by the wind, but they do not set into the terrain unless the terrain is ready to receive them. Claude Bernard (1927)

Bernard is right: the pathogen is nothing, the *terrain* is everything. Louis Pasteur, on his deathbed

Florence Nightingale, the nineteenth-century pioneer of nursing as a profession, also emphasizes the importance of the conditions in which diseases develop:

Is it not a continual mistake to look upon diseases, as we do now, as separate entities . . . instead of looking upon them as reactions of kindly Nature against the conditions in which we have placed ourselves? I was brought up by scientific men to believe that smallpox was a thing of which there was once a specimen in the world, which went on propagating itself in a perpetual chain of descent . . . and that smallpox would not begin itself any more than a new dog would begin without there having been a parent dog. Since then I have seen with my own eyes . . . smallpox growing up in first specimens, either in closed rooms or in overcrowded wards, where it could not by any possibility have been 'caught' but must have begun. Nay, more, I have seen diseases begin, grow and pass into one another . . . I have seen, for instance, with a little overcrowding, continued fever grow up, and with a little more, typhus, and all in the same ward or hut. For diseases, as all experience shows, are adjectives, not noun substances. The specific disease doctrine is the grand refuge of weak, uncultured, unstable minds, such as now rule in the medical profession. There are no specific diseases; there are specific disease conditions. Florence Nightingale (1860)

Lowered Resistance

Is disease just a random attack with no meaning for the patient? Perhaps inner disharmony encourages disease. Perhaps we become ill because of machinations between body and mind:

What then was life? It was warmth ... a fever of matter ... the existence of the actually impossible to exist, of a half-sweet, half-painful balancing, or scarcely balancing, in this restricted and feverish process of decay and renewal, upon the point of existence. It was not matter and it was not spirit, but something between the two, a phenomenon conveyed by matter, like the rainbow on the waterfall, and like the flame. Thomas Mann (1996)

Illness and death make ashes of all the fire that flamed for us. Charles Baudelaire

The human body is like a bakery with a thousand windows. We are looking into only one window when we are investigating one particular aspect of a disease. Bela Schick

When our health is disturbed our natural healing powers work to re-establish harmony. There is a patient and a healer within each of us, and when we are sick they are both active:

Even while still in the womb, man is burdened with the potentialities of every disease, and is subject to them. And because all diseases are inherent in his nature, he could not be born alive and healthy if an inner physician were not hidden in him ... Just as in the outside world a mason can wreck and has tools for this purpose, just as another mason has tools for building, so both – the destroyer and the preserver – have tools for wrecking and tools for building ... the body possesses the high art of wrecking and also restoring. Paracelsus (1951)

Disease is a permanent possibility which is constantly being prevented by the energies of life working within us:

In everyday life a human constantly becomes a bit indisposed and then must cure himself. The point is that all of us are a little sick when thirsty or hungry, and we cure ourselves by drinking and eating. Hunger is the beginning of an illness. Rudolf Steiner (1981)

The nervous–sensory system is the basis of conscious waking life which continually erodes the life and vitality of the physical body. This is replenished during sleep when physical and etheric forces assert themselves in the metabolism. From the tension between these two opposing dynamics, illness in the human being arises. Health is a sign that a temporary equilibrium has been established between the two systems. Dr James Dyson (1991)

> The vital spirits they're called, and well they may,
> For when they fail, man turns to his clay.
> Anne Bradstreet (1969)

Making Ourselves III

> O rose! thou art sick!
> The invisible worm
> That flies in the night
> In the howling storm,
>
> Has found out thy bed
> Of crimson joy;
> And his dark secret love
> Does thy life destroy.
> William Blake (1794)

The 'invisible worm' could be part of ourselves:

> I must have been incredibly simple or drunk or insane
> To sneak into my own house and steal money
> To climb over the fence and take my own vegetables
> But no more – I've gotten free of that ignorant fist
> That was pinching and twisting my secret self.
> Rumi (sound recording)

There is a dark part of ourselves which seems to want to cause us trouble:

> a total stranger one black day
> knocked living the hell out of me –
>
> who found forgiveness hard because
> my (as it happened) self he was
>
> – but now that fiend and i are such
> immortal friends the others each.
> e. e. cummings (1991)

> With curious art the brain too finely wrought,
> Preys on herself, and is destroy'd by thought.
> Charles Churchill (1763)

He is beset by conflict between his biology and his sociology. Abraham Meyerson

There is a kind of 'dis-ease' which is rooted in our inner conflicts:

Don't tell me what type of disease the patient has, tell me what type of patient has the disease. Sir William Osler (1904)

A man is his own disease. Taylor Caldwell (1959)

Man is a museum of diseases. Mark Twain (1916)

Self-knowledge can sometimes help:

> O wad some Pow'r the giftie gie us
> To see oursels as others see us!
> It wad frae monie a blunder free us.
> Robert Burns (1993)

Illnesses tell us what we are. Italian proverb

The Sickness Within

I am not a mechanism, an assembly of various sections.
And it is not because the mechanism is working wrongly, that I
  am ill.
I am ill because of wounds to the soul, to the deep emotional
  self . . .
D. H. Lawrence (1906)

I have learned that for every condition in our lives, there is a need for
it. Otherwise we would not have it. The symptom is only an outer
effect. We must go within to dissolve the mental cause. This is why
willpower and discipline do not work. They are only battling the
outer effect. It is like cutting down the weed instead of getting the
root out. Louise Hay (1984)

Disease is in essence the result of conflict between soul and mind –
so long as our souls and our personalities are in harmony all is joy
and peace, happiness and health. It is when our personalities are led
astray from the path laid down by the soul, either by our own worldly
desires or by the persuasion of others, that a conflict arises. Dr Edward
Bach (1987)

Is there any evidence which supports this view? Statistics tell us that more
heart attacks occur between 8 and 9 o'clock in the morning and especially
on Monday morning. Statistics also reveal that the incidence of heart attacks
does not correlate with the expected risk factors, but does correlate with
job dissatisfaction:

Your health is bound to be affected, if day after day you say the
opposite of what you feel, if you grovel before what you dislike and
rejoice at what brings you nothing but misfortune. Our nervous system
isn't just a fiction, it's part of our physical body, and our soul exists
in space and is inside us, like the teeth in our mouth. It can't be forever
violated with impunity. Boris Pasternak (1995)

To know what you prefer instead of humbly saying Amen to what
the world tells you you ought to prefer, is to have kept your soul
alive. Robert Louis Stevenson (1877)

Much of Western life denies the values which heart and soul hold dear.

As we rush around chasing misguided dreams, our souls are starving, and life loses its purpose:

A man can get caught between an outer life whose meaning is draining away and an inner life dominated by lions enraged from lack of nourishment. Michael Meade (1993)

Meaningless is equivalent to illness. C. G. Jung (1987)

A neurosis must be understood, ultimately, as a suffering of a soul which has not discovered its meaning . . . *About a third of my cases* are not suffering from any clinically definable neurosis but from the senselessness and aimlessness of their lives. C. G. Jung (1966a)

It puzzles me terribly why these things should come. But do you know what I think? I think it's because one isn't just vulgarly selfish enough, vulgarly *physically* selfish, self-keeping and self-preserving. One wastes one's common flesh too much: then these microbes, which are the pure incarnation of invisible selfishness, pounce on one. D. H. Lawrence (1991)

8

The Meaning of Illness

In illness . . . we float with the sticks on the stream, helter-skelter with the dead leaves on the lawn, irresponsible and disinterested and able, perhaps for the first time in years, to look round, to look up . . . Virginia Woolf (1967)

Is There Any Meaning in Illness?

The statistics on heart attacks in the last chapter seem to suggest that illness does have a meaning.

Illness has meaning; and to understand how it obtains meaning is to understand something fundamental about illness, about care, and perhaps about life generally. Arthur Kleinman (1988)

Orthodox medicine no longer has time to consider this question:

The technology of medicine has run way ahead of thinking about the nature of and meaning of illness. 'Why has this man fallen ill?' is a question that is simply never asked in western society. Yet the question is relevant. It is important to know why this man fell ill, why he fell ill when he did, and why it was he and not his twin brother. Glin Bennet (1979)

But if we are interested in healing the soul as well as the body, this question must be asked:

It is because I trust in your healing and my healing and the healing of humanity of which we each comprise a part that I offer here for your consideration some possible answers to those impossible questions: 'Why me? Why this? Why Now?' Robin Norwood (1995)

A Cloud with a Silver Lining?

'Tis healthy to be sick sometimes. Henry Thoreau (1906)

What doesn't kill me makes me stronger. Friedrich Nietzsche (1968)

Perhaps some illnesses are helpful in the maintenance of health:

There are many . . . who are perpetually taking remedies for irremediable pains and aches. They *ought* to have headaches and backaches and stomach-aches; they are not well if they do not have them. To expect them to live without frequent twinges is like expecting a doctor's old chaise to go without creaking; if it did, we might be sure the springs were broken. Oliver Wendell Holmes (1866)

The challenge, then, is to regard illness as an experience that may have some value:

Death is no enemy of life; it restores our sense of the value of living. Illness restores the sense of proportion that is lost when we take life for granted. To learn about value and proportion we need to honour illness, and ultimately to honour death. Arthur Frank (1991)

Minor illnesses especially can be useful:

There are illnesses of which one must not try to be cured because they alone protect us from more serious ills. Marcel Proust (1995)

A case could be made, I think, for viewing the various viruses involved in these minor but impressive illnesses as a set of endangered species, essentially *good* for the human environment . . . It is a good thing for people to have, from time to time, something real to complain about, a genuine demon. It is also a good thing to be laid up once in a while, compelled by nature to stop doing whatever else and to take to bed. It is an especially good thing to have a fever and the malaise that goes with a fever, when you know that it will be gone in three or four days but meanwhile entitles you to all the privileges of the sick; bed rest, ice water on the bed table, aspirin, maybe an ice bag on the head or behind the neck, and the attentions of one's solicitous family. Sympathy; how many other opportunities turn up in a lifetime to engage the sympathy and concern of others for something which is not your fault and will surely be gone in a few days? Preserve the grippe, I say, and find some way to insert it into the medical curriculum of all medical students . . . Lewis Thomas (1992)

Illness is to a large extent rooted in eternal causes. The Christian doctrine of original sin and the Buddhist Four Noble Truths teach that human life is wounded in its essence, and suffering is in the nature of things. We are wounded simply by participating in human life, by being children of Adam and Eve. To think that the proper or natural state is to be without wounds is an illusion. Any medicine motivated by the fantasy of doing away with woundedness is trying to avoid the human condition. Thomas Moore (1992)

What the Soul Wants in Illness

It's easy to suffer for a cause or a mission; this ennobles the heart of the person suffering. Paulo Coelho (1996)

The soul longs for release from bodily entrapment. It may prefer illness to health, because in illness the bonds between body and soul are relaxed, the soul is let loose into new landscapes, and the suppressed and unhappy parts of ourselves get a chance to speak:

> SOUL
> What magic could me thus confine
> Within another's grief to pine,
> Where, whatsoever it complain,
> I feel, that cannot feel, the pain,
> And all my care itself employs,
> That to preserve which me destroys:
> Constrain'd not only to endure
> Diseases, but what's worse, the cure:
> And ready oft the port to gain,
> Am shipwrecked into health again?
>
> BODY
> But physic yet could never reach
> The maladies thou me dost teach:
> Whom first the cramp of hope does tear,
> And then the palsy shakes of fear;
> The pestilence of love does heat,

Or hatred's hidden ulcer eat;
Joy's cheerful madness does perplex,
Or sorrow's other madness vex;
Which knowledge forces me to know,
And memory will not forgo.
What but a soul could have the wit
To build me up for sin so fit?
So architects do square and hew,
Green trees that in the forest grew.

Andrew Marvell (1681)

To respect the soul's needs often involves going against our normal assumptions. The soul is linked to our wounded selves, and wants us to go with the illness – to steer into the skid, to feel the pain fully. In this way we can meet unfulfilled parts of ourselves, and learn the meaning of our illness:

In a sense, people have within them a room or a chamber where a part of them is always lying incurably ill. The illness comes from being separated from the beauty and full range of life that the soul desires. The cure can be found in the place of greatest loss and fear . . .

Before most people can admit to the incurable condition of their souls, they have to describe and diagnose and prescribe and recast it many times. But this condition speaks most clearly when it is permitted to be simply incurable. The only way to treat the condition is to get everything out of the way and allow the sickness to speak for itself. It can only be heard when all the possible cures have been eliminated and its incurability has been admitted. The soul sickness needs permission to be the strange story that it declares itself to be. Michael Meade (1993)

Illness as a Messenger from the Wilderness Within

Even accidents can be the soul's cries for help:

In one three-month period, I encountered three middle-aged men, each of whom had fallen from a rooftop and broken numerous bones. Each was incapacitated, stuck in bed, pulled out of the flow of life. Two of them volunteered that they had been resisting a voice telling them that they needed a career or life change. An inner voice had been saying, 'You'd better stop what you're doing.' They had known that a change had been called for, but they couldn't stop. When we hear this voice, it often doesn't make sense to us – or not enough sense until everything crashes down. Michael Meade (1993)

These messages cannot be ignored indefinitely:

Until the soul has got what it wants it must fall ill again. James Hillman (1964)

From this angle, illness is trying to tell us something:

In sickness the mind reflects upon itself. Pliny (1991)

Diseases . . . crucify the soul of man. Robert Burton (1621)

I have learnt much from disease which life would never have taught me anywhere else. J. W. von Goethe

Accepting and Learning from Pain

I said to my soul, be still, and let the dark come upon you . . . T. S. Eliot (1944)

Experience the pain. Let us not fear its impact on ourselves or others. We will not shatter, for we are not objects that will break. Nor will we get stuck in this pain, for it is dynamic, it flows through us. Drop our defences, let us stay present in its flow, express it – in words, movements and sounds. Joanna Macey (1983)

I have some right to defend my own pain . . . I like to have an attack of pain now and then. Henri Matisse

Going with pain, illness and suffering is a way of renewal better understood in other cultures. Here an African shaman with a European PhD explains what his culture has to tell us:

For the Dagara elder, pain is the result of resistance to something new – something towards which an old dispensation is at odds . . . Body complaint is understood as the soul's language relayed to us. A person in pain is being spoken to by that part of himself that knows only how to communicate in this way . . . In other words, the soul is moving old furniture out and bringing in new furniture. Whether this eventually works out well is another question. We do not always allow ourselves to work through pain . . . In this context, a body in pain is a soul in longing. To shut down the pain is to override the call of the soul. When this happens it is a repressive measure taken against oneself, which has sombre consequences. Malidoma Patrice Some (1993)

Surprisingly enough, Hippocrates, the father of western medicine, says something similar:

A wise man should consider that health is the greatest of human blessings, and learn how by his own thought to derive benefit from his illnesses. Hippocrates (1978)

Our culture does not follow this advice; the result is empty lives and desperate souls:

Pain loses its referential character if it is dulled, and generates a meaningless, questionless residual horror ... The new experience that has replaced dignified suffering is artificially prolonged, opaque, depersonalized maintenance. Increasingly pain-killing turns people into unfeeling spectators of their own decaying lives. Ivan Illich (1975)

Respecting Our Illnesses

Illness could be considered a western form of meditation. We have no tradition of stopping to re-evaluate our lives. Dr Rachel Naomi Remen (1997)

To insure oneself from hurt is to insure oneself from growth. Georg Groddeck (1979)

Illness is a negative feedback system: it is telling us what we need to stop doing. If we look at illness that way, then it has great value. It might be telling us that we need to mollify our work habits, to rest or to question what we are doing. O. Carl Simonton

Some patients testify that illness has taught them something and made them better people:

A change came over me which I believe is irreversible. Questions of prestige, of political success, of financial status, became all at once unimportant. In those first hours when I realized I had cancer, I never thought of my seat in the Senate, of my bank account, or of the destiny of the free world ... My wife and I have not had a quarrel since my illness was diagnosed. I used to scold her about squeezing the toothpaste from the top instead of the bottom. [I now have] a new appreciation of things ... For the first time I think I actually am savouring life. Senator Richard Neuberger (quoted in Frank, 1962)

By opening to a view of adversity as a path to our healing we can feel trust even in times of despair. We can trust not only that the time will pass, but that our suffering has meaning and purpose and dignity. Robin Norwood (1995)

For affliction is a treasure and scarce any man hath enough of it. No man hath affliction enough, that is not matured and ripened by it, and made fit for God by that affliction. John Donne (1987)

... I am reminded once again not just of the meaningfulness of illness, but the solace to be gained from acknowledging that meaning, rather than seeing our afflictions as random. If we see disease as an opportunity for the revelation and unfolding of our individual blueprint, we heal inwardly and sometimes outwardly as well. As one workshop member said, 'We need to heal from the inside out.' Bernie S. Siegel (1993)

It is surprising how many writers share this view; disease brings with it possibilities of healing:

We are healed of a suffering only by experiencing it to the full. Marcel Proust (1995)

Happiness is beneficial to the body but it is grief that develops the powers of the mind. Marcel Proust (1995)

The world breaks everyone and afterward many are strong at the broken places. Ernest Hemingway (1929)

A Crisis is an Opportunity

A seasonable fit of illness is an excellent medicine for the turbulence of passion. Such a reformation had the fever produced in the economy of his thoughts, that he moralized like an apostle and projected several prudential schemes for his future conduct. Tobias Smollett (1751)

Many a man's life is lengthened by a sharp illness; and this is in several ways. In the first place he is laid up, out of reach of all external mischief and exertion, he is like a ship put in the dock for repairs; time is gained. A brisk fever clarifies the entire man, if it is beaten and does not beat him; it is like cleaning a chimney by setting it on fire; it is perilous but thorough. Then the effort to throw off the disease often quickens and purifies and corroborates the central powers of life; the flame burns more clearly; there is a cleanness, so to speak, about all the wheels of life. John Brown (1858–82)

There is a Chinese saying that a crisis is an opportunity. In chaos theory it is at times of disintegration that a new order can emerge. In illness, there is the opportunity to achieve a new level of health.

> Sickness is wholesome, and crosses are but curbs
> To check the mule, unruly man,
> They are heaven's husbandry, the famous fan
> Purging the floor which chaff disturbs . . .
> Henry Vaughan (1871)

And as Jesus passed by, he saw a man which was blind from his birth. And his disciples asked him, saying, Master, who did sin, this man or his parents, that he was born blind? Jesus answered, neither hath this man sinned, nor his parents: but that the works of God should be made manifest in him. John ix, 1

All this is not a call to seek pain masochistically; rather, by facing pain and accepting it, we bring it to an end. Resistance intensifies and prolongs the pain.

Accept the material of life. Do not criticize your part in the play. Study it, understand it, and then play it, sick or well, rich or poor, with courage, and with proper grace. Austen Fox Riggs

> Those who flow with life well know
> They need no other force:
> They feel no wear, they heed no tear,
> Require no mending or repair.
> Lao-tzu

9

Responding to Illness

Illness is the doctor to whom we pay most heed. Marcel Proust (1995)

The Easy Health of Childhood

Illness and ageing can bring nostalgia for the health we took for granted in childhood:

> Oh for boyhood's painless play,
> Sleep that wakes in laughing day,
> Health that mocks the doctor's rules,
> Knowledge never learned of schools.
> John Greenleaf Whittier (1889)

But there is a danger that these memories can become a morbid fascination:

> Happy those early days, when I
> Shin'd in my Angel-infancy!
> Before I understood this place
> Appointed for my second race,
> . . . But felt through all this fleshly dress
> Bright shoots of everlastingness.

O how I long to travel back,
And tread again that ancient track!
. . . Some men a forward motion love,
But I by backward steps would move . . .
Henry Vaughan (1871)

What peaceful hours I once enjoy'd!
How sweet their mem'ry still!
But they have left an aching void,
The world can never fill.
William Cowper (1779)

And there are traumas as well as joys in childhood:

If you remember your past too well you start blaming it for your present. Look what they did to me, that's what caused me to be like this, it's not my fault. Permit me to correct you; it probably *is* your fault. And kindly spare me the details. Julian Barnes (1991)

This poem suggests something akin to 'false memory syndrome':

O memory thou fond deceiver,
Still importunate and vain,
To former joys recurring ever,
And turning all the past to pain.
Oliver Goldsmith (1801)

Merciful Forgetfulness

I recovered my senses after three weeks of delirium, and was told I had had a very bad typhoid fever, and nearly died, and was still very sick. All of which seemed rather curious, for I remembered nothing of it. Louisa May Alcott (1874)

The nineteenth-century American poet, Emily Dickinson, describes how an ability to hide away unbearable pain is built into our bodies and minds; it is a survival mechanism:

There is a pain so utter –
It swallows substance up
Then covers the abyss with trance –
So memory can step
Around – across – upon it
As one within a swoon
Goes safely where an open eye
Would drop him – bone by bone.

Emily Dickinson (1983)

Some pain is too much to bear, and memory steps over it. Childhood sexual abuse is a perfect example of this. Often it is only several decades later that the person can face that experience or even remember it. Through all those years it swallows up some of the substance of that person.

Pains and disease of the mind are cured only by forgetfulness – reason but skins the wound, which is perpetually liable to fester again.
Erasmus Darwin (1789)

Guilt

The approach to illness suggested in some parts of this book could make us feel guilty. If our illnesses are part of ourselves, have we caused them, and are we to blame?

It adds to the affliction that relapses are (and for the most part justly) imputed to ourselves, as occasioned by some disorder in us; and so we are not only passive but active in our own ruin; we do not only stand under a falling house, but pull it down upon us . . . John Donne (1987)

But this guilt is a product of some unfortunate conditioning:

For those of us who do not have . . . a direct physiological cause, the answer to 'why me?' is bound to involve guilt. As the prayer I learned as a child in church said, 'We have left undone those things which we ought to have done, And we have done those things which we ought not to have done, And' – here's the punch line – 'there's no health in us.' What terrible words to put in the mind of a child. Arthur Frank (1991)

At worst, such attitudes can lead us to condemn ourselves and our whole lives:

His mental sufferings were due to the fact that in the night . . . the thought had suddenly come into his head: 'What if in reality my whole life has been wrong?' . . . It struck him that those scarcely detected inclinations of his to fight against what the most highly placed people regarded as good, those scarcely noticeable impulses which he had immediately suppressed, might have been the real thing, and all the rest false . . . And as soon as he admitted that thought his exasperation returned and with it the agonizing physical suffering . . . Leo Tolstoy (1960)

But in the end Ivan Ilyich goes beyond guilt, accepts his fate and forgives himself. He realizes the meaning of his sickness and dies at peace.

His anguish continues relentlessly until, shortly before his death, Ivan Ilyich comes upon a stunning truth: *he is dying badly because he has lived badly.* In the few days remaining to him, Ivan Ilyich undergoes a dramatic transformation that is difficult to describe in any other terms than personal growth. Irvin D. Yalom (1980)

Accepting Responsibility Without Guilt

You do not have to be good.
You do not have to walk on your knees
for a hundred miles through the desert repenting.
You only have to let the soft animal of your body
love what it loves.
Mary Oliver (1986)

There is a fine but important line between feeling guilty about being ill and taking responsibility for healing oneself:

Responsibility and guilt are not the same things. Neither are disease and failure. Bernie S. Siegel (1993)

Every disease is a doctor. Irish proverb

Sick people should not be made to feel guilty.

It cannot be overemphasized that this . . . most important question – why did you need this illness? – must be asked constructively, not

as a way of saying, 'Look what a mess you've made of your life.' Bernie
S. Siegel (1986)

Legitimizing the patient's illness experience . . . is a key task in the
care of the chronically ill. Arthur Kleinman (1988)

The point is not to blame ourselves for illness but to see it as an opportunity
for renewal.

As long as you fight a symptom, it will become worse. If you take
responsibility for what you are doing to yourself, how you produce
your symptoms, how you produce your illness, how you produce your
existence – the very moment you get in touch with yourself – growth
begins, integration begins. Fritz Perls (1976)

Whoever, like me, sees in illness a vital expression of the organism,
will no longer see it as an enemy . . . in the moment that I realize that
the disease is a creation of the patient, it becomes for me the same
sort of thing as his manner of walking, his mode of speech, his facial
expression, the movement of his hands . . . a significant symbol of the
powers that rule him . . . Georg Groddeck (1979)

Was not my sly strength, my insistent specialness, somehow linked
to my psoriasis? Might it not be the horrible badge of whatever in me
was worth honouring? Only psoriasis could have taken a very average
little boy, and furthermore a boy who loved the average, the daily,
the safely hidden, and made him into a prolific, adaptable, ruthless
enough writer. What was my creativity, my relentless need to produce
but a parody of my skin's overproduction? Was not my thick literary
skin which shrugged off rejection slips and patronizing reviews by
the sheaf a superior version of my poor vulnerable own, and my
shamelessness on the page a distraction from my real shame? . . .
Dualism, indeed, such as existed between my skin and myself, appeared
to me the very engine of the human. And with my changeable epiderm
came a certain transcendent optimism; like a snake I shed many skins.
John Updike (1989)

IO

The Search for Healing

For every ill beneath the sun
There is some remedy or none,
If there be one, resolve to find it;
If not, submit and never mind it.
Anon

Starting the Search

The first cry of pain through the primitive jungle was the first call for a medicine. Victor Robinson (1931)

O what a miracle to man is man,
Triumphantly distressed! what joy, what dread!
Alternately transported, and alarmed!
What can preserve my life? or what destroy?
Edward Young (1742−4)

When the realization comes that we really are ill, then the fact must be faced and something must be done. This awareness shocks and undermines us, but also gives the impetus to look for healing:

An awareness of illness is part of the price that man first paid and still pays for his self-consciousness. This awareness increases the pain or disability. But . . . with this self-consciousness arises the possibility of treatment, of medicine. John Berger and Jean Mohr (1967)

I was burned out from exhaustion, buried in the hail,
Poisoned in the bushes an' blown out on the trail,
Hunted like a crocodile, ravaged in the corn.
'Come in,' she said, 'I'll give you shelter from the storm.'
Bob Dylan (1974, 1975a)

Like . . . nomads we live in a desert with many lonely travellers who are looking for a moment of peace, for a fresh drink and a sign of encouragement so that they can continue their mysterious search for freedom. Henri Nouwen (1972)

A primeval fear makes something lurch deep within us, and then we seek help:

The earliest sensation at the onset of illness, often preceding the recognition of identifiable symptoms, is apprehension. Something has gone wrong, and a glimpse of mortality shifts somewhere deep in the mind. It is the most ancient of fears. Something must be done, and quickly. Come, please, and help, or go, please, and find help. Hence the medical profession. Lewis Thomas (1992)

First of all we need an explanation, a context for our sickness, to make it less threatening:

The decision to seek medical consultation is a request for interpretation . . . Patient and doctor together reconstruct the meaning of events in a shared mythopoesis . . . Once things fall in place; once experience and interpretation appear to coincide; once the patient has a coherent 'explanation' which leaves him no longer feeling the victim of the inexplicable and the uncontrollable the symptoms are, usually, exorcized. Leon Eisenberg (1981)

We hope there is some magic way of getting well again:

People on their ailments are not always interesting, far from it. But we all hope for a – must I say the word – recipe, we all believe, however much we know we shouldn't, that maybe somebody's got that recipe and can show us how not to be sick, suffer and die. Nan Shin (1986)

The world offers help to us:

The lord hath created medicines out of the earth and he that is wise will not abhor them. *Apocrypha*, Ecclesiasticus xxxviii, 4

The garden is the poor man's apothecary. German proverb

But we may have to wait for this salvation:

For ilka ill there is a cure,
Be it in root or leaf or floo'r,
An' aft-times roon aboot the door.

Tho' it grows free for all mankind
Lang may ye seek afore ye find.

David Rorie (in Downie, 1995)

Hope

Hope is the physician of all misery. Irish proverb
Hope is always important:

> To suffer woes which Hope thinks infinite;
> To forgive wrongs darker than Death or Night;
> To defy power which seems omnipotent;
> To live and bear, to hope, till Hope creates
> From its own wreck the thing it contemplates;
> Neither to change nor falter nor repent:
> This, like thy glory, Titan! is to be
> Good, great and joyous, beautiful and free;
> This is alone Life, Joy, Empire and Victory.

P. B. Shelley (1977)

In listening to our terminally ill patients we were always impressed that even the most accepting, the most realistic patients left the possibility open for some cure, for the discovery of a new drug or the 'last-minute success in a research project' . . . it is this glimpse of hope that maintains them through days, weeks, or months of suffering. It is the feeling that all this must have some meaning, will pay off eventually if they can only endure it for a little while longer. It is the hope that occasionally sneaks in, that all this is just like a nightmare and not true; that they will wake up one morning to be told that the doctors are ready to try out a new drug which seems promising, that they will use it on him and he may be the chosen, special patient, just as the first heart-transplant patient must have felt that he was chosen to play a very special role in life. It gives the terminally ill a sense of a special mission in life which helps them maintain their spirits, will enable them to endure more tests when everything becomes such a strain – in a sense it is a rationalization for their suffering at times; for others it remains a form of temporary but needed denial.

No matter what we called it, we found that all our patients maintained a little bit of it and were nourished by it in especially difficult times. They showed the greatest confidence in the doctors who allowed for such hope – realistic or not – and appreciated it when hope was offered in spite of bad news. This does not mean that doctors have to tell them a lie; it merely means we share with them the hope that something unforeseen may happen, that they may have a remission, that they will live longer than expected. If a patient stops expressing hope, it is usually a sign of imminent death. They may say, 'Doctor, I think I have had it,' or 'I guess this is it,' or they may put it like the patient who always believed in a miracle, who one day greeted us with the words 'I think this is the miracle – I am ready now and not even afraid any more.' All these patients died within twenty-four hours. While we maintained hope with them, we did not reinforce hope when they finally gave it up, not with despair but in a stage of final acceptance. Elizabeth Kubler-Ross (1979)

That helpless voice is always there, crying out for help:

> In the time of my confession,
> In the hour of my deepest need,
> When the pool of tears beneath my feet
> Flood every newborn seed
> There's a dyin' voice within me
> Reaching out somewhere,
> Toiling in the danger
> And in the morals of despair.
> Bob Dylan (1981)

When all the doors in this world seem to be closed, we have to look beyond it. In the next piece a disabled boy hopes that healing and help against his enemies will come from the Skallagrigg, the mythical protector of the disabled:

Yes, the Skallagrigg would come, and the legions that were Rendel, and the armies that were Dilke, would quail before his anger and his power and his strength, and they would bow down before the love that he Eddie could command. And when that day came Eddie would be taken back and shown how to climb over the wooden fence past Apsham Wood, over into the meadows beyond which the Skallagrigg lives, and there he would be helped to stand at last and feel the winds, warm and soft, cold and violent, on his cheeks.

Yes, one day, one day the Skallagrigg would hear his cries, and come for him, to take him out of hell. William Horwood (1988)

Trust

His brow spreads large and placid, and his eye
Is deep and bright, with steady looks that still.
Soft lines of tranquil thought his face fulfil –
His face at once benign and proud and shy.
If envy scout, if ignorance deny,
His faultless patience, his unyielding will,
Beautiful gentleness and splendid skill,
Innumerable gratitudes reply.
His wise, rare smile is sweet with certainties
And seems in all his patients to compel
Such love and faith as failure cannot quell.
We hold him for another Herakles,
Battling with custom, prejudice, disease,
As once the son of Zeus with Death and Hell.
W. E. Henley (1992)

And one should not erode the mystique with which patients naturally endow healers:

The Catholic Church never explains anything and remains the strongest power in the world; the Protestant Church tries to explain everything and is crumbling to pieces. The less your patients know the truth, the better for them. It was never meant that the working of the organs of our body should be watched by the mind; to make your patients think about their illness is to tamper with the laws of Nature. Tell them that they must do so and so, take such and such a remedy in order to get better, and if they don't mean to obey you they must go to somebody else. Do not call on them except when they are in absolute need of you, do not talk too much to them or they will soon find you out and how little we know. Doctors, like royalties, should keep aloof as much as possible, or their prestige will suffer, we all look our best in a somewhat subdued light. Look at the doctor's own family, who always prefer to consult somebody else! Axel Munthe (1949)

Suspicion

When the clever doctor fails, try one less clever. Bechuanaland proverb

There may be more than one direction to look for help, and one cannot know beforehand which treatment will turn out to be best. On top of that uncertainty there is another. For as long as there has been healing there have been charlatans, well-meaning people out of their depth, and varying mixtures of ignorance, inexperience, prejudice and cynicism:

I tremble at the thought of what would have happened to me had I fallen into the hands of one of the other leading surgeons in Paris in those days. Old Papa Richet in the other wing of Hôtel Dieu would surely have made me die of gangrene or blood poisoning, it was his speciality, it was rampant all over his medieval clinic. The famous Professor Péan, the terrible butcher of Hôpital St Louis, would have chopped off both my legs on the spot and thrown them on the top of some stumps of arms and legs, half a dozen ovaries and uteruses and various tumours, all in a heap on the floor of his amphitheatre besmeared with blood like a slaughterhouse. Then, his enormous hands still red with my blood, he would have plunged his knife with the dexterity of a conjurer into his next victim, half conscious under insufficient anaesthesia, while half a dozen others, screaming with terror on their brancards, were waiting their turn of torture. The massacre *en masse* at an end, Péan would wipe the sweat from his forehead, rub a few spots of blood and pus from his white waistcoat – he always operated in evening dress – and with a: *Voilà pour*

aujourd'hui, Messieurs! he would rush out of the amphitheatre . . .
Axel Munthe (1949)

The combination of fear and hope can make us gullible. Various writers
have criticized the healing profession's response to this:

Montaigne wrote bluntly concerning doctors: 'I have known
many a good man among them, most worthy of affection. I do not
attack them, but their art. It is only fear of pain and death, and a
reckless search for cures, which blinds us. It is pure cowardice that
makes us so gullible.' Molière made delightful fun of his doctors in
his century. Dickens had some affection but no great respect for the
doctors, most of them odd, bumbling eccentrics, who turned up as
minor but essential characters in all his novels. Shaw was a scathing
critic of medicine and its pretensions, clear into modern times. Lewis
Thomas (1992)

Cure to a physician is a pure accident, to the pathologist in his
laboratory almost a disappointment. The real thing is the excitement
of the chase, the opportunity for the exercise of precise talents, the
occasion for batting down a rival to supersede him, to strut, to boast
and to get on with one's fellows. Discovery is the great goal – and
the accumulation of wealth. William Carlos Williams (1967)

In the next piece, the question of quackery takes a surprising turn:

Of late an agitation had been started in the press to protest against
the steadily increasing number of foreign doctors in Paris, often, it was
hinted, not even provided with regular diplomas from well-recognized
universities. It resulted in an order by the Préfet de Police that all
foreign doctors were to present their diplomas for verification before
the end of the month . . . The Commissaire, who knew me slightly,
asked me if I knew a Doctor X . . . he was on their blacklist, he had
not presented himself with his diploma . . . he was said to be making
two hundred thousand francs a year . . . I heard the end of the story
a couple of months later from the Commissaire himself. Doctor X
had presented himself at the very last moment with a request for a
private interview with the Commissaire. Presenting his diploma as
MD of a well-known German university, he implored the Commissaire
to keep his secret, he said he owed his enormous practice to the
circumstance that he was considered by everybody to be a quack. Axel
Munthe (1949)

In any case, medical knowledge is never perfect. Here is an uncompromising opinion:

We were the ones who believed. We were the ones in ritual gloves and masks carrying the sacred surgical steel. So passive, not a spark of resentment, they were grateful to me for throwing their tits into the incinerator.

We don't do it any more, the treatment has changed, we regret that we did it so much, but when you tell people you know what's good for them particularly if you are a doctor, they will believe you . . .

I sent her for a mammogram. In those days we screened women for what we still call 'Their Own Good'. We made them feel irresponsible if they refused. The good doctor. The difficult patient. It wasn't until 1993 that the best of us admitted that for women under the age of fifty, a mammogram is notoriously unreliable, and that it might even serve to spread any few malignant cells deeper into the body. Jeannette Winterson (1995)

Refusing the Medication

The trouble with medicine today is we simply do not know enough, we are still a largely ignorant profession, faced by an array of diseases which we do not really understand, unable to do much beyond trying to make the right diagnosis, shoring things up whenever we can by one halfway technology or another (the transplantation of hearts, kidneys, livers and lungs are the only measures available when we lack any comprehension of the events responsible for the prior destruction of such organs). Lewis Thomas (1992)

Common sense tells us not to expect too much – but meanwhile our hearts are crying out for help. Here a naturopath and a novelist share a disillusioned view:

The basic fault of [drugs] is that they have no known connection with the disease process itself . . . drugs are wholly unlike nature's weapons . . . they tend to mask the difficulty, not eliminate it. They contaminate the internal environment [with side-effects], create dependence on the part of the patient, and often complicate the physician's job by erasing valuable clues as to the real source of the trouble. Roger Williams (1971)

Doctors are men who prescribe medicines of which they know little, to cure diseases of which they know less, to human beings of whom they know nothing. Voltaire

Some defiance may be advisable:

The world is full of Intuitive Diagnosticians and Vicarious Undertakers. Every third person I meet seems to know what ails me, and a good many of them have buried me so deep that they take it as a personal affront that I am still walking about. I have made up my mind to outlive all these vultures, just for spite . . . Robertson Davies (1986)

The only way I could get my surgeon, a seasoned professional, to talk about the details of and alternatives to the operation he was planning (which was never carried out and would have been unnecessary) was to refuse to sign the consent form. Arthur Frank (1991)

Would we go so far as to reject medicine altogether?

> By chase our long-lived fathers earned their food;
> Toil strung the nerves, and purifi'd the blood;
> But we, their sons, a pamper'd race of men,
> Are dwindled down to threescore years and ten.
> Better to hunt in fields, for health unbought,
> Than fee the doctor for a nauseous draught.
> The wise for cure on exercise depend;
> God never made his work for man to mend.
> John Dryden (1700)

Medical Fashions

The suspicions of this patient are unfounded:

Mrs Dollop became more and more convinced by her own asseveration, that Doctor Lydgate meant to let people die in the Hospital, if not to poison them, for the sake of cutting them up without saying by your leave or with your leave; for it was a known 'fac' that he had wanted to cut up Mrs Goby, as respectable a woman as any in Parley

Street, who had money in trust before her marriage – a poor tale for a doctor, who if he was good for anything should know what was the matter before you died, and not want to pry into your inside after you were gone. George Eliot (1871–2)

But sometimes we should be sceptical. For example medical procedures can change, and not always for good reason.

Appendicitis was just then much in demand among better-class people on the lookout for a complaint. All the nervous ladies had got it on the brain if not in the abdomen, thrived on it beautifully, and so did their medical advisers. So I drifted gradually into appendicitis and treated a great number of such cases with varied success. But when the rumour began to circulate that the American surgeons had started on a campaign to cut out every appendix in the United States, my cases of appendicitis began to fall off in an alarming way. Consternation.

'Take away the appendix! My appendix!' said the fashionable ladies, clinging desperately to their *processus vermicularis*, like a mother to an infant. 'What shall I do without it!'

'Take away their appendices, my appendices!' said the doctors, consulting gloomily the list of their patients. 'I have never heard such nonsense! Why there is nothing wrong with their appendices, I ought to know, I who have to examine them twice a week. I am dead against it!'

It soon became evident that appendicitis was on its last legs, and that a new complaint had to be discovered to meet the general demand. The faculty was up to the mark, a new disease was dumped on the market, a new word was coined, a gold coin indeed, COLITIS! It was a neat complaint, safe from the surgeon's knife, always at hand when wanted, suitable to everyone's taste. Nobody knew when it came, nobody knew when it went away. I knew that several of my far-sighted colleagues had already tried it on their patients with great success . . . Axel Munthe (1949)

II

Places of Healing

Here, at whatever hour you come, you will find light and help and human kindness. Inscription outside Albert Schweitzer's hospital

Hospitals, Patients and Visitors

If we follow the normal course in deteriorating health, then hospital is the next stage:

When he waked up, he had a sense of the whole big mechanism of the hospital, cut off from the rest of the world, yet self-sufficient, like a boat or a train . . . There was a routine, and you saw a great deal of people you would probably never see again. Stephen Vincent Benét

One sees all human life flow in and out of the doors of a hospital:

The impression was neither of tragedy nor comedy . . . It was manifold and various; there were tears and laughter, happiness and woe; it was tedious and interesting and indifferent; it was as you saw it; it was tumultuous and passionate . . . It was life. W. Somerset Maugham (1915)

> Within these gray walls life begins and ends,
> Here, in this harbor, worn, sea-weary ships
> Drop anchor, as the fading sun descends,
> And new launched vessels start their outbound trips.
> E. E. Laughlin

A hospital is a living organism . . . its work is never done. John Shaw Billings (1890)

93

The following poem conveys the bewilderment of a close friend or relative as the sick person disappears into hospital and returns a changed person:

> Illness tossed you over the rails
> of our world –
> the huge hospital swallowed you
> then swam away
> to go through its routines with you
> deep and distant.
>
> I could no more than paddle in
> that element –
> but came often to watch from the shore
> and scan the surface.
>
> After a secret number of days
> and hidden nights,
> after fathomless hours enclosed
> in the whale's belly
> floating on tides of attention
> and murmurs of movement,
> the hospital will spit you out again
> at my feet . . .
>
> I begin to lead you home, only to discover
> we are on a foreign shore.
>
> Tessa Ransford (1984)

And this poem, written during a lunch break, observes the patient's experience of that 'foreign shore':

> Like gulls they are still calling –
> *I'll come again Tuesday. Our Dad*
> *Sends his love.* They diminish, are gone.
> Their world has received them,

As our world confirms us. Their debris
Is tidied into vases, lockers, minds.
We become pulses; mouthpieces
Of thermometers and bowels.

The trolley's rattle dispatches
The last lover. Now we can relax
Into illness, and reliably abstracted
Nurses will straighten our sheets,

Reorganize our symptoms. Outside,
Darkness descends like an eyelid.
It rains on our nearest and dearest
In car parks, at bus-stops.

Now the bed-bound rehearse
Their repertoire of movements,
The dressing-gowned shuffle, clutching
Their glass bodies.

Now siren voices whisper
From headphones, and vagrant
Doctors appear, wreathed in stethoscopes
Like South Sea dancers.

All's well, all's quiet as the great
Ark noses her way into the night,
Caulked, battened, blessed for her trip,
And behind, the gulls crying.

U. A. Fanthorpe (1986)

Abandoned Inmates

Milton gives us a blood-curdling description of a hospital:

> A Lazar-house it seemed, wherein were laid
> Numbers of all diseas'd, all maladies,
> Of ghastly spasm, or racking torture, qualms
> Of heart-sick agony, all feverous kinds,
> Convulsions, epilepsies, fierce catarrhs,
> Intestine stone and ulcer, colic pangs,
> Demonic frenzy, moping melancholy,
> And moonstruck madness, pining atrophy,
> Marasmus, and wide-wasting pestilence,
> Dropsies, and asthmas, and joint-racking rheums.
> Dire was the tossing, deep the groans, despair
> Tended the sick busiest from couch to couch.
> John Milton (1667)

Modern hospitals are nothing like that, but going into hospital is still a withdrawal from normal life:

The hard lump of his tumour – unexpected, meaningless and quite without use – had dragged him in like a fish on a hook and flung him on to this iron bed – a narrow mean bed, with creaking springs and an apology for a mattress. Having once undressed under the stairs and said goodbye to the family and come up to the ward, you felt the door to all your past life had been slammed behind you, and life here was so vile that it frightened you more than the actual tumour ... But the harmonious, exemplary Rusanov family, their well-adjusted way of life and their immaculate apartment – in the space of a few days all this had been cut off from him. It was now on the *other* side of his tumour. They were alive and would go on living whatever happened to their father. However much they might worry, fuss or weep, the tumour was growing like a wall behind him, and on this side he was alone. Alexander Solzhenitsyn (1968)

A patient withdraws from normal life, and is initiated into a new society:

One's own clothes are replaced by an anonymous white nightgown, one's wrist is clasped by an identification bracelet with a number. One becomes subject to institutional rules and regulations. One is no longer a free agent; one no longer has rights; one is no longer in the world-at-large. It is strictly analogous to becoming a prisoner and humiliatingly reminiscent of one's first day at school. One is no longer a person, one is now an inmate. Oliver Sacks (1989)

Life is a hospital in which every patient is possessed by the desire to change his bed. Charles Baudelaire

The next poem describes the sadness of long-term residents of modern institutions:

> Like children, when it's sunny they behave,
> Play ball-games on the grass, run the canteen
> Without much obvious embezzlement,
> Are regular with drugs, use no obscene
> Words to alarm the matron, kick the cat
> Only in private, go for jolly walks
> In healthy groups, return in time for tea,
> Cooperate in therapeutic talks.
>
> Like children, when it's rainy they are bad,
> Forgetful of the needs of indoor plants,
> Ignore their visitors, smoke endlessly,
> Confine their repartee to *won't* and *shan't*,
> Form tear-stained queues outside the nurses' room,
> Drink gin at night, and set fire to their sheets,
> Abscond, break windows, commit suicide,
> Involve us in their infantile defeats.
>
> Like parents, we don't take them seriously.
> We shrug their tantrums off as children's play,
> We speak to them in kindergarten tones,
> Deaf to the insult under all we say.
> And when they mimic adult games, and kiss,
> And talk of marriage, we applaud *How nice!*
> Joyfully yoking two unstable minds,
> Our wedding gift a birth-control device.

Like anchorites, they guard their silent cells,
Devoted to the rituals of despair.
The blood-soaked stone walls are inviolable,
And laymen cannot penetrate to share
The vigils these abandoned saints must bear,
Who straddle the irreconcilable
Vaults of mankind in our hygienic air,
And gasp their litanies to our dry bells.
U. A. Fanthorpe (1986)

This is the time of day when we in the Men's Ward
Think 'One more surge of the pain and I give up the fight',
When he who struggles for breath struggles less strongly;
This is the time of day which is worse than the night.

A haze of thunder hangs on the hospital rose-beds,
A doctor's foursome out on the links is played,
Safe in her sitting-room Sister is putting her feet up;
This is the time of day when we feel betrayed.

Below the window, loads of loving relations
Rev in the car-park, changing gear at the bend,
Making for home and a nice big tea and the telly:
'Well, we've done what we can, it can't be long till the end.'

This is the time of day when the weight of the bedclothes
Is harder to bear than the sharp incision of steel.
The endless anonymous croak of a cheap transistor
Intensifies the lonely terror I feel.
John Betjeman (1970)

Sanctuaries of Healing

They that can wander at will where the works of the Lord are reveal'd
Little guess what joy can be got from a cowslip out of the field;
Flowers to these 'spirits in prison' are all they can know of the spring

They freshen and sweeten the wards like the waft of an Angel's
  wing.

Alfred Lord Tennyson

Hospitals are the temples of medicine. Henry Sigerist

The first hospitals were indeed temples to the gods and goddesses of
healing. A natural and beautiful environment assists with healing, and so does
nursing:

The trained nurse has become one of the great blessings of humanity,
taking a place beside the physician and the priest, and not inferior to
either in her mission. Sir William Osler (1904)

> In the tendrils of their care
> I leaf and learn again.
>
> Life's better for knowing them
> they're fun, down to earth, so young.
> I may be mother but now
> I'm utterly dependent.
>
> They wash me, change me, talk to me,
> wipe away the spills and tears
> clean pin-sites, understand
> but do not pander to my pain.

Cicely Herbert (1992)

In the book *The Secret Garden* the little boy Colin is cured by honesty,
friendship, love and nature. The secret garden is the hospital and sanctuary,
Mary is the nurse and Dickon, the child of nature, is the healing priest:

'How is he?' Dr Craven asked Mrs Medlock rather irritably when
he arrived. 'He will break a blood vessel in one of those fits some day.
The boy is half insane with hysteria and self-indulgence.'

'Well, sir,' answered Mrs Medlock, 'you'll scarcely believe your eyes
when you see him. That plain, sour-faced child that's almost as bad as
himself has just bewitched him. How she's done it there's no telling.
The Lord knows she's nothing to look at and you scarcely ever hear her
speak, but she did what none of us dare do. She just flew at him like

a little cat last night, and stamped her feet and ordered him to stop screaming, and somehow she startled him so that he actually did stop, and this afternoon – well, just come and see, sir. It's past crediting.'

The scene which Dr Craven beheld when he entered his patient's room was indeed rather astonishing to him. As Mrs Medlock opened the door he heard laughing and chattering . . .

Then they saw Dr Craven and stopped. Mary became quite still and Colin looked fretful.

'I am sorry to hear you were ill last night, my boy,' Dr Craven said, a trifle nervously. He was rather a nervous man.

'I'm better now – much better,' Colin answered, rather like a rajah. 'I'm going out in my chair in a day or two if it is fine. I want some fresh air.'

Dr Craven sat down by him and felt his pulse and looked at him curiously.

'It must be a very fine day,' he said, 'and you must be very careful not to tire yourself.'

'Fresh air won't tire me,' said the young rajah.

As there had been occasions when this same young gentleman had shrieked aloud with rage and had insisted that fresh air would give him cold and kill him, it is not to be wondered at that his doctor felt somewhat startled.

'I thought you didn't like fresh air,' he said.

'I don't when I'm by myself,' replied the rajah; 'but my cousin is going out with me . . . My cousin knows how to take care of me. I am always better when she is with me. She made me better last night. A very strong boy I know will push my carriage.'

Dr Craven felt rather alarmed . . .

'He must be a strong and a steady boy,' he said, 'and I must know something about him. Who is he? What is his name?'

'It's Dickon,' Mary spoke up suddenly. She somehow felt that everyone who knew the moor must know Dickon. And she was right, too. She saw that in a moment Dr Craven's serious face relaxed into a relieved smile.

'Oh, Dickon,' he said. 'If it is Dickon you will be safe enough. He's as strong as a moor pony, is Dickon.'

'And he's trusty,' said Mary. 'He's th' trustiest lad i' Yorkshire.'

She had been talking Yorkshire to Colin and she forgot herself.

'Did Dickon teach you that?' asked Dr Craven, laughing outright.

'I'm learning it as if it was French,' said Mary, rather coldly. 'It's like a native dialect in India. Very clever people try to learn them. I like it and so does Colin.'

'Well, well,' he said. 'If it amuses you perhaps it won't do you any harm. Did you take your bromide last night, Colin?'

'No,' Colin answered, 'I wouldn't take it at first, and after Mary made me quiet she talked me to sleep – in a low voice – about spring creeping into a garden.'

'That sounds soothing,' said Dr Craven, more perplexed than ever and glancing sideways at Mistress Mary, sitting on her stool and looking down silently at the carpet. 'You are evidently better, but you must remember –'

'I don't want to remember,' interrupted the rajah, appearing again. 'When I lie by myself and remember I begin to have pains everywhere, and I think of things that make me begin to scream because I hate them so. If there was a doctor anywhere who could make you forget you were ill instead of remembering it, I would have him brought here,' and he waved a thin hand which ought to have been covered with royal signet rings made of rubies. 'It is because my cousin makes me forget that she makes me better.'

Dr Craven had never made such a short stay after a 'tantrum'; usually he was obliged to stay a very long time and do a great many things. This afternoon he did not give any medicine or leave any new orders, and he was spared any disagreeable scenes. When he went downstairs he looked very thoughtful, and when he talked to Mrs Medlock in the library she felt that he was a much puzzled man.

'Well, sir,' she ventured, 'could you have believed it?'

'It is certainly a new state of affairs,' said the doctor. 'And there's no denying it is better than the old one.'

'I believe Susan Sowerby's right – I do that,' said Mrs Medlock. 'I stopped in her cottage on the way to Thwaite yesterday, and had a bit of a talk with her. And she says to me, "Well, Sarah Ann, she mayn't be a good child, an' she mayn't be a pretty one, but she's a child, an' children needs children." We went to school together, Susan Sowerby and me.'

'She's the best sick nurse I know,' said Dr Craven. 'When I find her in a cottage I know the chances are I shall save my patient.' Frances Hodgson Burnett (1967)

Later we find that the healing continues:

'Father,' he said, 'I'm Colin. You can't believe it. I scarcely can myself, I'm Colin.'

Like Mrs Medlock, he did not understand what his father meant when he said hurriedly: 'In the garden! In the garden!'

'Yes,' hurried on Colin. 'It was the garden that did it – and Mary and Dickon and the creatures – and the Magic. No one knows. We kept it to tell you when you came. I'm well; I can beat Mary in a race. I'm going to be an athlete.'

He said it all so like a healthy boy – his face flushed, his words tumbling over each other in his eagerness – that Mr Craven's soul shook with unbelieving joy.

Colin put out his hand and laid it on his father's arm.

'Aren't you glad, father?' he ended. 'Aren't you glad? I'm going to live for ever and ever and ever!'

Mr Craven put both his hands on the boy's shoulders and held him still. He knew he dared not even try to speak for a moment.

'Take me into the garden, my boy,' he said at last. 'And tell me all about it.'

And so they led him in. Frances Hodgson Burnett (1967)

Great Mother Nature can heal our souls:

> Wild air, world-mothering air,
> Nestling me everywhere . . .
> This needful, never spent,
> And nursing element;
> My more than meat and drink,
> My meal at every wink . . .
> Gerard Manley Hopkins (1967)

The whole earth is our hospital . . .
T. S. Eliot (1944)

12

When Healing Comes

But soul-rejoicing health again returns,
The blood meanders gently in each vein,
The lamp of life renewed with vigour burns,
And exiled reason takes her seat again . . .
Christopher Smart (1756)

Intimations of Improvement

In the deserts of the heart
Let the healing fountains start.
W. H. Auden (1967)

Is there a turning-point, a moment in time when the healing begins?

Next day, a junior physio, evening student
at the City Lit of circus skills,
bows to my feet and juggles, just for me.
From such pleasures healing comes.
I crow for joy and swear I will recover.
Cicely Herbert (1992)

The really decisive moments in psychotherapy, as every patient or psychotherapist who has ever experienced them knows, are unpredictable, unique, unforgettable, always unrepeatable and often indescribable. R. D. Laing (1965)

The healing may start with certainty and confidence:

The genius of American medicine, I said, was brought home to the world in 1981 with the attempted assassination of President Reagan. Who will ever forget the modesty, good humour, and extraordinary skilfulness communicated on the television screen by the physicians overseeing the treatment of the president's wounds? Not the slightest sense of mystification, withholding, or confusion – only a sense of order and organization of information, a relaxed, firm plan of action, a rationale for every decision. There were the extraordinary diagrams of the bullet's trajectory inside the president's body – the whole thing entirely like the space mission. Jacob Needleman (1992)

Or perhaps the early signs of improvement are unreliable. Is the treatment really working? Is it safe to celebrate wholeheartedly? Can we trust that the new health will not disappear again?

It was like sucking in freedom, like inhaling the blue sky; I became an addict. I carried my knobbly little plastic lifeline everywhere, bulging my pockets and letting lint and sand work into its crevices, especially into the tiny hole, no bigger than a mustard seed, where the life-giving mist shot out, with that delightful admonitory hiss. Sometimes I inhaled grit and pellets of fluff but I didn't care. Without my Medihaler, I felt lost and naked; once, in the middle of the second fairway of a golf course, I had to walk off and drive home and get the thing. After that, I kept one in my golf bag. I kept another in the glove compartment of my car, and several more in drawers around the house. And so for some years I enjoyed the illusion of chemical-induced security . . . The Medihaler had its limits. As with the psoriasis, cures wore off, leaving me again alone with my defective, imperilled self. John Updike (1989)

The good news may come mixed with the prospects of further suffering. This provisional salvation is unsettling:

When you told me that for six months I would need to have both my legs in casts, I simply nodded. Suddenly everything became silent in me. I wanted to obey something, something bigger than myself, but all I could feel was fear rising up within me, making me so intensely silent. So this was what it was like to actually be part of nature, reality.

You didn't make pleasantries, you didn't even explain what was wrong with me. (I learned later that the tendons had separated from the heel; the specialist had recommended surgery; you chose otherwise.)

You gave me a pair of crutches and told me to practise with them before coming to your office the following day to have the casts put on.

Why didn't you say anything more? And if there was nothing to say, why did you not simply dismiss me from the room? There were so many other patients waiting, old people, people much sicker than I. Why did you simply allow me to sit on that table while you briskly went about some business or other in the room, shuffling charts, taking down X-rays, washing your hands? I know what was happening in me – did you know it too? Did you sense it? I was finding my own strength. I believe you sensed that. My own strength.

Eventually, I slid down from the table and walked out of the examining room, crutches in hand. I felt empty, and alive.

'See you tomorrow,' you said.

I turned to look at you. Your eyes did not give an inch. All they did was to confirm my state of inner presence. Jacob Needleman (1992)

When Healing Comes: The Turning-point

Tolling for the aching ones whose wounds could not be nursed,
For the countless confused, accused, misused, strung-out ones an'
   worse,
An' for every hung up person in the whole wide universe,
An' we gazed upon the chimes of freedom flashing.
Bob Dylan (1964)

Here an asthmatic celebrates and prolongs the relief he gets from his medication:

Out of my pocket I pulled the little blood-red pill box, as elegantly ovoid as an eighteenth-century snuff box. Under the little wad of cotton wool the precious yellow pills lay, the full rich yellow of golden eggs in a fairy story. I broke one in half down the line of its shallow incision and slipped it under my tongue. Its sickly sweetness filled my mouth. I let it dissolve as slowly as possible to prolong the anticipation of relief, its delight not to be too greedily grasped at. Ferdinand Mount (1992)

A poet celebrates his recovery from a serious illness:

But, O immortals! What had I to plead
When death stood o'er me with his threat'ning lance,
When reason left me in the time of need,
And sense was lost in terror or in trance?
My sick'ning soul was with my blood inflamed,
And the celestial image sunk, defaced and maimed.

But soul-rejoicing health again returns,
The blood meanders gently in each vein,
The lamp of life renewed with vigour burns,
And exiled reason takes her seat again –
Brisk leaps the heart, the mind's at large once more,
To love, to praise, to bless, to wonder and adore.

The virtuous partner of my nuptial bands
Appeared a widow to my frantic sight;
My little prattlers, lifting up their hands,
Beckon me back to them, to life, and light;
I come, ye spotless sweets! I come again,
Nor have your tears been shed, nor have ye knelt in vain.

My feeble feet refused my body's weight,
Nor would my eyes admit the glorious light,
My nerves convulsed shook fearful of their fate,
My mind lay open to the powers of night.
He pitying did a second birth bestow,
A birth of joy – not like the first of tears and woe.

Christopher Smart (1756)

The Joy of Newfound Health

See the wretch that long has tossed,
On the thorny bed of pain,
At length repair his vigour lost,
And breathe, and walk again.

The meanest floweret of the vale,
The simplest note that swells the gale, –
The common sun, the air, the skies, –
To him are opening paradise.

Thomas Gray (1787)

Once recovery is assured there is the time of convalescence, when healing is consolidated. This is the time for returning to the world:

The patient ceases to feel the presence of illness and the absence of the world, and comes to feel the absence of his illness and the full presence of the world. Oliver Sacks (1973)

Carry me out
Into the wind and the sunshine,
Into the beautiful world.

W. E. Henley (1992)

Laurie Lee describes the sensation of being a fragile newborn thing. The newborn person is full of wonder, and feels the world intensely:

After fever my body and head felt light, like a piece of dew-damp vegetable. The illness had emptied me so completely now I seemed bereft of substance. Being so long in that sunless, fever-spent room, I was filled with extraordinary translations. I felt white and blood-drained, empty of organs, transparent to colour and sound, while there passed through my flesh the lights of the window, the dust-changing air, the fire's bright hooks, and the smooth lapping tongues of the candle. Heat, reflection, whispers, shadows, played around me as though I was glass. I seemed to be bodiless, printed flat on the sheets, insubstantial as a net in water. What gross human wastes, dull jellies, slack salts I had been purged of I could not say; but my senses were now turned to such an excruciating awareness that they vibrated to every move of the world, to every shift and subsidence both outdoors and in, as though I were renewing my entire geography.

When I woke in the mornings, damp with weakness, the daylight was milk of paradise; it came through the windows in beaming tides, in currents of green and blue, bearing debris of bird-song, petals, voices, and the running oils of the sky. Its light washed the room of night and nightmare and showed me the normal day, so that waking was a moment of gratitude that savages must have felt. The bedroom objects removed their witch masks and appeared almost sheepishly ordinary. The boarded walls shone with grains and knots; the mirror recorded facts; the pictures, framed in the morning's gold, restored me their familiar faces. I sighed and stretched like a washed-up sailor who feels the earth safe beneath him, wild seas wiped away, green leaves around, deliverance miraculously gained.

So each morning at dawn I lay in a trance of thanks. I sniffed the room and smelt its feathers, the water in the wash-jug, the dust in the corners, kind odours of glass and paper, the dry stones facing the windowsills, bees bruising the geranium leaves, the pine in the pencil beside my bed, the dead candle, and the fire in the matchstick. But I also sensed, without needing to look, the state of the early day: the direction of the wind, how the trees were blowing, that there were cows in the fields or not, whether the garden gate was open or shut, whether the hens had yet been fed, the weight of the clouds in the invisible sky, and the exact temperature of the air. As I lay in my bed I could sense the whole valley by the surfaces of my skin, the turn of the hour, the set of the year, the weather, and the life to come. A kind of pantheist grandeur made me one with the village, so that I felt part of its destination; and washed of my fever, ice-cold but alive, it seemed I would never lose it again . . . Laurie Lee (1962)

At the beginning of illness we have to adapt to a new reality, and at the end another adjustment is required. We now learn to enjoy life again:

Who can describe the pleasure and delight, the peace of mind and soft tranquillity, the sickly boy felt in the balmy air, and among the green hills and rich woods of an inland village. Charles Dickens (1838)

My first well day – since many ill
I asked to go abroad,
And take the sunshine in my hands
And see the things in pod –

A'blossom just when I went in
To take my chance with pain –
Uncertain if myself, or He,
Should prove the strongest one.
Emily Dickinson (1983)

Measure your health by your sympathy with morning and spring. If there is no response in you to the awakening of nature . . . know that the morning and spring of your life are past. Henry Thoreau (1906)

I enjoy convalescence. It is the part that makes illness worthwhile. George Bernard Shaw (1921)

He brought me into a deep remembering garden
And I was like one that wakes from a dream of pain
To hear the cry of a thrush at evening
And the sound of a brook, and the whisper of Eden again.
Alfred Noyes (1950)

Rebirth after Illness

With how much speed
Doth health with smiles upon her countenance spread,
And breathe again her influence round his head;
Roused by her touch, he wakes to life once more,
With pleasures which he never felt before.
(For who, that has not felt the loss of health,
Can measure its inestimable wealth?)
Samuel Bartlett Parris (1829)

One may feel the unspeakable joy of life at these times, such as mystics and poets describe:

For it is not altogether ill with the invalid after all. If it is only rarely that anything penetrates vividly into his numbed spirit, yet, when anything does, it brings with it a joy that is all the more poignant for its very rarity. There is something pathetic in these occasional returns of glad activity of heart. In his lowest hours he will be stirred and awakened by many such; and they will spring perhaps from very trivial sources; as a friend once said to me, the 'spirit of delight' comes often on small wings. For the pleasure that we take in beautiful nature is essentially capricious. It comes sometimes when we least look for it; and sometimes when we expect it most certainly, it leaves us to gape joyless for days together, in the very homeland of the beautiful. We may have passed a place a thousand times and one; and on the thousand and second it will be transfigured, and stand forth in a certain splendour of reality from the dull circle of surroundings; so that we see it 'with a child's first pleasure', as Wordsworth saw the daffodils by the lakeside. Robert Louis Stevenson (1891)

The end of an illness is most satisfactory if it brings a new zest for life:

Out of such abysses, from such severe sickness one returns newborn, having shed one's skin, more ticklish and malicious, with a more delicate taste for joy, with a more tender tongue for all good things, with merrier senses, with a second dangerous innocence in joy, more childlike and yet a hundred times subtler than one has ever seen before. Friedrich Nietzsche (1974)

The following pieces of writing describe recovery as a symbolic rebirth or an awakening from a dream:

I have had three births; one natural, when I came into the world; one supernatural, when I entered into the ministry; and now a preternatural birth, in returning to life from this sickness. John Donne (1987)

I am my own blank page to write upon
Here it is and I can write peacock finery
Choosing all the colours, bright or dull
Or I can write nothing at all
But it is me who writes now
Me who shapes, who grows
And me who dances myself alive again.
Joy Adams

Between this sleeping and waking I lived ten generations and grew weak on my long careers, but when I surfaced at last from its endless delirium the real world seemed suddenly dear. While I slept it had been washed of fever and sweetened, and now wrapped me like a bell of glass. For a while, refreshed, I heard its faintest sounds: streams running, trees stirring, birds folding their wings, a hill-sheep's cough, a far gate swinging, the breath of a horse in a field. Below me the kitchen made cosy murmurs, footsteps went up the road, a voice said Goodnight, a door creaked and closed – or a boy suddenly hollered, animal-clear in the dark, and was answered far off by another. I lay moved to stupidity by these precious sounds as though I'd just got back from the dead. Laurie Lee (1962)

> And so long as you haven't experienced
> This: to die and so to grow,
> You are only a troubled guest
> On the dark earth.
> F. W. von Goethe (1814)

Recovery deserves a ceremony. Many aboriginal peoples have re-entry rituals during which a person who has been stigmatized is purified. These rituals are a rebirth; afterwards life can begin anew. Each of my critical illnesses ended with a medical event that could have been given a ritual value. But physicians, the high priests of our time, have let themselves be reduced to mere medical technicians. They act as if they are unaware of the power of their interventions to change the body's symbolic value. Both the patient and the physician are thus deprived of the spiritual experience of illness. Because ritual self-awareness is excluded from the system, it takes longer to work out one's own terms of re-entry. Arthur Frank (1991)

> Six hours a day I lay me down
> Within this tub, but cannot drown.
>
> The ice cap at my frigid neck
> Has served to keep me with the quick.

This water heated like my blood,
Refits me for the true and good.

Within this primal element
The flesh is willing to repent.

I do not laugh; I do not cry;
I'm sweating out the will to die.

My past is sliding down the drain;
I soon will be myself again.
Theodore Roethke (1986)

This new health can be a phoenix rising out of an awful lot of ashes:
My body was a toxic waste dump, but it was also living a miracle
. . . My existence was a wonder, living it an adventure. I could believe
in prevailing until the sun rose. The blessing was that I was seeing
life, face to face. Arthur Frank (1991)

13

The Ways of Healing

The office of medicine is but to tune this curious harp of man's body and to reduce it to harmony. Francis Bacon (1605)

Healing for Body and Soul

What is going on behind the scenes when healing comes? What is actually happening in the recesses of body and soul? Is recovery from illness merely a physiological change, or is there something more mysterious?

But what is healing? Is it merely the return to a familiar and satisfying life? I think not. To me it is the place of, as T. S. Eliot wrote, 'the intersection of the timeless with time'. This rapprochement is more than poetic awareness. It is an alchemy within our cells. Healing is a glimpse into the universal process of incarnation. Our very flesh vibrates with a larger connectedness to life. Richard Moss (1989)

The explanations for the healing processes that take place within the cells of our bodies tend to increase our sense of wonder rather than reduce it:

Gaze upon the skin as I have, through a microscope brightly, and tremble at the wisdom of God, for here is a magic tissue to suit all seasons. Two layers compose the skin – the superficial epidermis and, deeper, the dermis. Between is a plane of pure energy where the life-force is in full gallop. Identical cells spring full-grown ... to form an unbroken line over the body ... this number marches in well-stepped soldiery, gallantly summoned to a sacrifice beyond its ken ... let the skin be cut or burned, and the brigade breaks into a charge, fanning out laterally across the wound, racing to seal off the defect. The margins are shored up; healing earthworks are raised, and guerrilla squads of invading bacteria are isolated and mopped up. Hurrah for stratified squamous epithelium! Richard Selzer (1982)

There is a source of vitality, a fountain of health and well-being, within us:

> There was a time when, though my path was rough,
> This joy within me dallied with distress,
> And all misfortunes were but as the stuff
> Whence fancy made me dreams of happiness:
> For hope grew round me like the twining vine,
> And fruits, and foliage, not my own seemed mine.
> S. T. Coleridge (1802)

The next piece describes how we are healed of past traumas:

In times of healing, the events of the past become illumined with the energy of the present: we feel the old hurts anew and can mourn and rage and do the undone work that remains to release ourselves. Starhawk (1987)

This sort of experience is so good we should not have to be sick to partake of it:

True healing means drawing the circle of our being larger and becoming more inclusive, more capable of loving. In this sense, healing is not for the sick alone, but for all humankind. Richard Moss (1989)

Sources of the Gift

> A thing of beauty is a joy forever:
> Its loveliness increases; it will never
> Pass into nothingness; but still will keep
> A bower quiet for us, and a sleep
> Full of sweet dreams, and health, and quiet breathing.
> John Keats (1969)

The medical treatments that help us recover our health are many and various. We feel a profound gratitude to the herbal poultice or the enormous machine, to the skills of the osteopath or the spiritual healer. But the next quotation reminds us of Paracelsus' words – 'the physician is only the servant of nature':

Neither [medicine or surgery] can do anything but remove obstructions, neither can they cure; nature alone cures. Surgery removes the bullet out of the limb, which is the obstruction to cure, but nature heals the wound. Florence Nightingale (1860)

> Hippocrates in his aphorism, as Galen writeth sure,
> Saith four things are needful to every kind of cure.
> The first, saith he, to God belongeth the chief part,
> The second to the surgeon who doth apply the art.
> The third unto the medicine that is Dame Nature's friend,
> The fourth unto the patient, with whom I here will end.
> How then may a surgeon appoint a time, a day or hour,
> When three parts of the cure are quite without his power?
> William Clowes (1596)

Nature has her own doctor in every limb. Paracelsus (1951)

Miraculous results can come when human healers work with the forces of nature, the *vis medicatrix naturae*:

> This day relenting God
> Hath placed within my hand
> A wondrous thing; and God
> Be praised. At his command,
>
> Seeking his secret deeds
> With tears and toiling breath,
> I find thy cunning seeds,
> O million-murdering Death.
>
> I know this little thing
> A myriad men will save.
> O Death, where is thy sting?
> Thy victory, O Grave?
> Sir Ronald Ross (1897)

Herbal medicines are one source of healing. Each herb has a special 'virtue', a characteristic of its own which gives it the power to heal. Here the 'personalities' of two herbs are described:

> Vallisner[1] sits, upturns her tearful eyes,
> Calls her lost lover, and upbraids the skies;
> For him she breathes the silent sigh, forlorn,
> Each setting day, for him each rising morn.
>
> With fierce distracted eye Impatiens stands,
> Swells her pale cheeks, and brandishes her hands,
> With rage and hate the astonish'd groves alarms,
> And hurls her infants from her frantic arms.
> Erasmus Darwin (1789)

> The patient needs a magic pill:
> So the doctor will and yes he will prescribe
> the usual dew from a banana leaf; poppies and
> honey too; ten snowflakes or something whiter
> from the bole of a tree; the clearest water
> ever, melting ice from a mountain lake;
> sunlight from waterfall's edge, rainbow smoke;
> tears from eyelashes of the daughter.
> Dannie Abse (1989)

In this healing, from the New Testament, the 'virtue' comes direct from Christ:

And a certain woman, which had an issue of blood twelve years, and had suffered many things of many physicians, and had spent all that she had, and was nothing bettered, but rather grew worse, when she had heard of Jesus, came in the press behind, and touched his garment. For she said, if I may touch but his clothes, I shall be whole. And straightway the fountain of her blood was dried up; and she felt in her body that she was healed of that plague. And Jesus, immediately

---

1. Vallisner has roots at the bottom of rivers and by means of a flexible spiral stem keeps its flower on the surface even if the depth of water changes rapidly.

knowing in himself that virtue had gone out of him, turned him about in the press, and said, Who touched my clothes? And his disciples said unto him, Thou seest the multitude thronging thee, and sayest thou, Who touched me? And he looked round about to see her that had done this thing. But the woman fearing and trembling, knowing what was done in her, came and fell down before him, and told him all the truth. And he said unto her, Daughter, thy faith hath made thee whole; go in peace, and be whole of thy plague. Mark vi, 25

Now we go from the sublime to the ridiculous; this is a cure for 'composer's block':

And now I am delighted; the transition is unbelievably successful, with quite a wonderful combination of two themes. Heavens, how much can be achieved by the right sort of biscuits! – Biscuits! that is the proper remedy for composers when they get stuck – but they must be the right kind. Richard Wagner

Healing, Scientific and Sacred

Doctor-poet Dannie Abse asks whether the amazing powers of a stethoscope should lead us to venerate such wondrous instruments:

> Through it,
> over young women's tense abdomens,
> I have heard the sound of creation
> and, in a dead man's chest, the silence
> before creation began.
>
> Should I
> pray therefore? Hold this instrument in awe . . . ?

Dannie Abse (1989)

The next poem has no respect for scientific medicine:

Physician art thou? – one, all eyes,
Philosopher! – a fingering slave,
One that would peep and botanize.
Upon his mother's grave?

William Wordsworth (1969)

Ironically, a doctor writing prose gives the more poetic view of medicine:

I am committed to the idea that a surgeon should avoid being a
technocrat by all means, even if surgery has to be thought of in
religious terms; that the doctor and the patient are pilgrims. Together
they are in a search for the miracle of healing. Richard Selzer (1981)

The same writer describes Yeshi Donden, the personal physician of the
Dalai Lama, at work:

His eyes are closed as he feels for the pulse. In a moment he has
found the spot, and for the next half hour he remains thus,
suspended above the patient like some exotic golden bird with
folded wings, holding the pulse of the woman beneath his fingers,
cradling her hand in his. All the power of the man seems to be drawn
down into this one purpose . . . And I know that I, who have palpated
a hundred thousand pulses, have not felt a single one. Richard Selzer
(1982)

And in the next passage an asthmatic prefers his inhaler to his tablets. He
treats his inhaler as something sacred:

I preferred the puffer. The dark amber glass with its delicate curved
nozzle, the orange-red bulb, the sinister little bottle containing the
fluid – this was my hookah, my passport to nirvana. The anticipation
of sure relief as I put the cold glass to my lips, the faint sickly smell
before the first clean puff of vapour, like inhaling the mist of a winter
morning, a mist which had been somewhat doctored, the instantaneous
lengthening and taming of the spasms, so that their rapid brutal
clutchings faded into harmless undulating sighs, growing louder,
melodious almost, as they became less intense, less frequent, finally
settling into a low gravelling mouth-organ drone, and within my chest
sweet peace. Ferdinand Mount (1992)

The Healing Power of Images, Words and Sounds

I wish that I might go from door to door,
And lay my hand on every heart that's sore;
And say sweet words and comfort lids that weep.

Havelock Ellis

I wish I could take language
And fold it like cool, moist rags. I would lay words on your forehead.
I would wrap words on your wrists.

Julia Cameron (1995)

We all know that words can wound, and sometimes words can heal:

What made Wordsworth's poems a medicine for my state of mind was that they expressed not mere outward beauty but states of feeling, and of thought coloured by feeling . . . J. S. Mill (1873)

Images also have this power:

To the extent that I managed to translate the emotions into images – that is to say, to find the images which were concealed in the emotions – I was inwardly calmed and reassured. Had I left those images hidden in the emotions, I might have been torn to pieces by them. C. G. Jung (1987)

Perhaps music can also influence our health. The following passage celebrates this power and offers an explanation. Music is able

not only to expel the greatest griefs, but it doth extenuate fears and furies, appeaseth cruelty, abateth heaviness; and, to such as are watchful, it causeth quiet rest . . . it takes away spleen and hatred . . . and it cures all irksomeness and heaviness of the soul . . . because the spirits about the heart take in that trembling and dancing air into the body, are moved together and stirred up with it, or else the mind, as some suppose harmonically composed, is roused up at the tunes of music. And 'tis not only men that are so affected, but almost all other creatures. Robert Burton (1621)

This is a kind of sympathetic magic:

There is in souls a sympathy with sounds,
And as the mind is pitch'd the ear is pleased

With melting airs, or martial, brisk or grave;
Some chord in unison with what we hear
Is touched within us, and the heart replies.
... With easy force it opens all the cells
Where memory slept. Wherever I have heard
A kindred melody, the scene recurs,
And with it all its pleasures and its pains.
William Cowper (1785)

Taking Time Off

What dream of wealth am I chasing?
When I am at one with myself
All the world belongs to me.
Peter Adams

Recreation is literally re-creation of ourselves. We have to listen carefully to hear that voice within that is longing for the mountains, or whatever is our own source of replenishment.

To keep a lamp burning we have to keep putting oil in it. Mother Teresa (1993)

We need primitive nature, the First Man in ourselves, it seems, as the lungs need air and the body food and water; yet we can only achieve it by a slinking, often shameful, back-door entrance. Sir Laurens van der Post (1968)

My help is in the mountain
Where I take myself to heal
The earthly wounds that people give to me
I find a rock with sun on it
And a stream where the water runs gentle
And the trees which one by one give me company
So must I stay for a long time
Until I have grown from the rock
And the stream is running through me
And I cannot tell myself from one tall tree.

Then I know that nothing touches me
Nor makes me run away.
My help is in the mountain
That I take away with me.

Earth cure me. Earth receive my woe. Rock strengthen me. Rock receive my weakness. Rain wash my sadness away. Rain receive my doubt. Sun make sweet my song. Sun receive the anger from my heart. Nancy Wood (1972)

In Nature we rest in a great parental embrace. The simple radiance of nature becomes holy:

... what is left of true wilderness, what is left of the world that is near the original blueprint of creation, are the only true churches left in life. Sir Laurens van der Post (1962)

> Wild air, world-mothering air,
> Nestling me everywhere ...
> This needful never spent,
> And nursing element;
> My more than meat and drink,
> My meal at every wink ...
> Gerard Manley Hopkins (1967)

Another form of spiritual renewal is going into retreat:

> I have desired to go
> Where springs not fail,
> To fields where flies no sharp and sided hail
> And a few lilies blow.
>
> And I have asked to be
> Where no storms come,
> Where the green swell is in the havens dumb,
> And out of the swing of the sea.
> Gerard Manley Hopkins (1967)

An episode of illness can give us some time for unravelling our lives. Here a healer teaches her apprentice:

Sometimes life is too difficult to be lived, so it's better to be sick for a bit. 'So what happens then?' You have to tease out the pain – in their minds that is – like teasing burrs out of wool. Monica Furlong (1987)

We may feel ambivalent about such self-analysis:

> Self-contemplation is a curse
> That makes an old confusion worse.
>
> Recumbency is unrefined
> And leads to errors in the mind.
>
> Long gazing at the ceiling will
> In time induce a mental ill.
>
> The mirror tells some truth, but not
> Enough to merit constant thought.
>
> He who himself begins to loathe
> Grows sick in flesh and spirit both.
>
> Dissection is a virtue when
> It operates on other men.
>
> Theodore Roethke (1986)

Health from Within

I may not hope from outward forms to win
The passion and the life, whose fountains are within.
S. T. Coleridge (1802)

> Care to our coffin adds a nail, no doubt,
> And every grin so merry draws one out.
> John Wolcot (1789)

Once precious health has been regained, we start to wonder how to preserve it. We learn that our bodies gradually destroy themselves in the microscopic toil of keeping us alive, while our life-forces do repair and maintenance work:

> To wear out heart, and nerves, and brain,
> And give oneself a world of pain,
> Be eager, angry, fierce, and hot,
> Imperious, supple – God knows what
> . . . It is not in itself a bliss,
> Only it is precisely this
> That keeps us all alive.
> Arthur Hugh Clough (1869)

> By chase our long-liv'd fathers earn'd their food;
> Toil strung the nerves and purifi'd the blood:
> But we, their sons, a pamper'd race of men,
> Are dwindl'd down to threescore years and ten.
> John Dryden (1700)

> The blood, the fountain whence the spirits flow,
> The generous stream that waters every part,
> And motion, vigour, and warm life conveys
> To every particle that moves or lives;
> This vital fluid through unnumbered tubes
> Poured by the heart, and to the heart again
> Refunded; scourged for ever round and round;
> Enraged with heat and toil, at last forgets
> Its balmy nature; virulent and thin
> It grows; and now, but that a thousand gates
> Are open to its flight, it would destroy
> The parts it cherished and repaired before.
>   . . . but what the vital force
> Of plastic fluids hourly batters down,
> That very force, those plastic particles
> Rebuild: so mutable the state of man.
> For this the watchful appetite was given,

Daily with fresh materials to repair.
This unavoidable expense of life,
This necessary waste of flesh and blood.
Dr John Armstrong (1744)

How far does this process of self-repair and self-creation go?

... the simple fact that the will to do anything can and does, at a certain pitch of intensity set up by conviction of its necessity, create and organize new tissue to do it with ... If the weight-lifter, under the trivial stimulus of athletic competition, can 'put up a muscle', it seems reasonable to believe that an equally earnest and convinced philosopher could 'put up a brain'. Both are directions of vitality to a certain end. Evolution shows us this direction of vitality doing all sorts of things: providing the centipede with a hundred legs, and ridding the fish of any legs at all; building lungs and arms for the land and gills and fins for the sea ... offering us, we may say, our choice of any sort of bodily contrivance to maintain our activity and increase our resources. George Bernard Shaw (1921)

Through suffering we have to develop a higher self, which transcends the pain:

We get accustomed to mental as well as bodily pain, without for all that losing our sensibility to it. It becomes a habit of our lives and we cease to imagine a condition of perfect ease as possible for us. Desire is chastened into submission, and we are contented with our day when we have been able to bear our grief in silence and act as if we are not suffering. For it is at such periods that the sense of our lives, having visible and invisible relations beyond any of which our present or prospective self is the centre, grows like a muscle that we are obliged to lean on and exert. George Eliot (1859)

To learn to live with ourselves is healthy:

If you bring forth what is within you, what you bring forth will save you. If you do not bring forth what is within you, what is within you will destroy you. Gospel of Thomas (1977)

The hurt that a person feels in the midst of this modern culture should be taken as a language spoken to himself or herself by the body. And the meaning of such a language is found in doing something about the part of oneself that is not acknowledged. Malidoma Patrice Some (1993)

When a man has learned – and not on paper – how to remain alone with his suffering, how to overcome his longing to flee, then he has little left to learn. Albert Camus (1970)

Irene travels at great expense to Epidauros, visits Aesculapius in his temple, and consults him on her various ailments. To begin with she explains that she feels weary and worn out; and the god declares that this is because of the great distance she has just come. She says that she has no appetite in the evenings; the oracle orders her not to eat much. She adds that she is subject to insomnia; he advises not to take to her bed except at nights . . . 'My eyesight is failing,' Irene says. 'Get some glasses,' says Aesculapius. 'I'm failing myself,' she continues; 'I'm not as strong and healthy as I was.' 'That is because you are ageing.' 'But what way is there of curing this lassitude?' 'The quickest way, Irene, is to die as your mother and your grandmother have done.' 'Son of Apollo,' Irene cries, 'what advice are you giving me? Is that all the wisdom men speak of, for which the whole world reveres you? What have you told me that is exceptional and mysterious? And didn't I already know all those remedies you have advised?' 'Then why did you not make use of them,' the god replies, 'without coming so far to find me, and shortening your days by a long journey?' Jean de La Bruyère (1688)

14

The Healer

If I can stop one heart from breaking
I shall not live in vain
If I can ease one Life the Aching
Or cool one Pain
Or help one fainting Robin
Unto his nest again
I shall not live in vain.

Emily Dickinson (1983)

He who would do good to another must do it in minute particulars:
General good is the plea of the scoundrel, hypocrite and flatterer.

William Blake (1804)

The Healing Relationship

A health professional is someone who has chosen to specialize in a difficult area of human experience, to carry a torch into the darkness:

It is our inability to communicate to another how we are locked within ourselves, unable to say the simplest thing of importance to one another ... that makes our lives like those of a litter of kittens in a woodpile. That gives the physician ... his opportunity. William Carlos Williams (1984)

Some healing comes simply from the presence of the healer. Here a young patient relaxes dream-like into the care of 'the great physician'. The 'great physician' is the archetypal healer, who is ready to guide the hand of mortal physicians and give inspiration to the patient.

I can see you now as I saw you when I was very young, I am frightened by something that is happening in me. There is pain and weariness. I seem unable to think and I don't know what I am or what my body is doing to me.

Then you appear in my room. I remember your voice, quiet and strong. Never in my house was a voice so quiet, so free of agitation. Immediately I felt something quiet in myself, some movement of opening and letting go. Alongside the fear and self-pity, there is now something inside of me that is not afraid. Suddenly I am two: a frightened child and a watchful presence.

You take my hand. I remember the pressure of your fingers around my wrist. I remember how you looked at me. No one ever looked at me like that. What were you seeing? Why did your look make me feel that I was in the world of men, not children?

Now you are exploring my body – mouth, eyes, chest. You turn me on my side and place the cold stethoscope against my back. What is there to listen to there? You turn me back again and lower the blankets. I am surprised that I feel no embarrassment. I watch your face as you probe and press, firmly, gently, sharply. When you cause pain, I make a sound, but without anger or hurt. With no one else do I react to pain in that way, simply as something physical, without emotion. Even when I'm alone, pain makes me emotional. But now I am only a watchful presence and a physical body. The frightened child, with nothing to feed on, has disappeared.

Your face is full of attention, full of listening. How I remember that face! No one ever looked at me or my body with such a face. How you trusted your power of listening, your state of attention. And how your trust brought into our house and into myself a movement towards a new order. I know now that this is why you devoted yourself to medicine even though you yourself didn't realize it. I know now that in your face so full of listening there was something a little bit like divinity, something I can now call love. But no one calls that love now. What stupid names people give it when it appears! We didn't call it love then, either; all we could do was to revere the role of the physician because down deep we sometimes sensed the mystery of that trust in total attention, the only thing in man that can meet life and death squarely, without cringing.

You pull the blankets up and stand over me. Gently you return me to the world of children and to ordinary time. You make a joke, you hand me a piece of candy. My mother appears at your side. You speak to her about me and tell her what needs to be done. She keeps glancing at me solicitously. I allow her concern to enter me, but only up to that luminous border within myself, behind which I now exist outside of fear and desire. As you leave you look at me again. Silently, I promise you, 'I will not allow anything to cross this border in myself.' And I then give my body over to my mother and her tender ministrations.

Shall I continue with other pictures of what you were like not so long ago? I want you to come back; we all want it; we all dream of it.

I can see you smiling indulgently at me as I write this. But wait, hear me out. I tell you that you yourself have forgotten what you stood for in people's lives. Perhaps you never really knew it – how could you? Like all of us, you are a product of the times. How could you know that your role was one of the very last surviving traces of the sacred in our world? Jacob Needleman (1992)

The relationship between healer and patient has tremendous possibilities:

So for me the practice of medicine has become the pursuit of a rare element which may appear at any time, at any place, at a glance. It can be most embarrassing. Mutual recognition is likely to flare up at a moment's notice. The relationship between physician and patient, if it were literally followed, would give us a world of extraordinary fertility of the imagination which we can hardly afford. William Carlos Williams (1984)

The Call to Heal

Whoever among us has through personal experience learned what pain and anxiety really are must help to ensure that those who out there are in bodily need obtain the help which came to him. He belongs no more to himself alone; he has become the brother of all who suffer. On the 'brotherhood of those who bear the mark of pain' lies the duty of medical work. Albert Schweitzer (1933)

I wish I'd have been a doctor,
Maybe I'd have saved some lives that had been lost,
Maybe I'd have done some good in the world
'Stead of burning every bridge I've crossed.
Bob Dylan (1983)

I don't think I should love him if he were well and happy, but
    you said he was ill – and alone . . .
Elizabeth Barrett Browning (1856)

A healer's calling is fundamentally simple. It comes from the desire to help others, to relieve suffering:

Now I wish I could write you a melody so plain
That could hold you dear lady from going insane
That could ease you and cool you and cease the pain
Of your useless and pointless knowledge.
Bob Dylan (1965)

We must all die. But that I can save [a person] from great torture, that I feel as my great and ever new privilege. Pain is a more terrible lord of mankind than death himself. Albert Schweitzer (1933)

Healers must believe that there is hope for the world:

Had? has it come? It has only dawn'd. It will come by and by.
O how could I serve in the wards if the hope of the world were a
    lie?
How could I bear with the sights and the loathsome smells of
    disease
But that He said, 'Ye do it to me, when ye do it to these'?
Robert Louis Stevenson

When we look back into the past we see an endless train of doctors on the march. Their dress, their language, their social position varies; their outlooks and their methods change from age to age . . . yet one and all, from the shamans of primitive tribes to the scientific physicians of our own day, are inspired by the same will. Henry E. Sigerist (1933)

But the basically simple mission of the healer has many ramifications and variations:

Lydgate was ambitious above all to contribute to enlarging the scientific, rational basis of his profession. The more he became interested in special questions of disease, such as the nature of fever or fevers, the more keenly he felt the need for that fundamental knowledge of structure which just at the beginning of the century had been illuminated by the brief and glorious career of Bichat, who died when he was one-and-thirty, but, like another Alexander, left a realm large enough for many heirs . . . George Eliot (1871–2)

Lydgate's ambition is to

pierce the obscurity of those minute processes which prepare human misery and joy, those invisible thoroughfares which are the first lurking-places of anguish, mania and crime. George Eliot (1871–2)

The Role of the Healer

The paths of pain are thine. Go forth
With healing and with hope.
John Greenleaf Whittier (1889)

Contained in the system of operations of any school of healing, there is the archetype of the healer. James Hillman (1964)

When fainting nature called for aid,
And hov'ring death prepared the blow,
His vig'rous remedy displayed
The power of art without the show.

In misery's darkest caverns known,
His useful care was ever nigh,
Where hopeless anguish poured his groan,
And lonely want retired to die,

No summons mocked by chill delay,
No petty gain disdained by pride,
The modest wants of ev'ry day
The toil of ev'ry day supplied.

Samuel Johnson (1783)

Being a healer, a health professional of whatever persuasion, demands great sacrifices and brings great rewards:

Men who suppress their feelings, but who feel
The painful symptoms they delight to heal;
Patient in all their trials, they sustain
The starts of passion, the reproach of pain;
With hearts affected, but with looks serene,
Intent they wait through all the solemn scene;
Glad if a hope should rise from nature's strife.
To aid their skill and save the lingering life;
But this must virtue's generous effort be,
And spring from nobler motives than a fee.

George Crabbe (1810)

The Work of the Healer

Perform all this calmly and adroitly, concealing most things from the patient while you are attending him. Hippocrates (1995)

Where the challenge is 'to save a lingering life' the stress factor is quite obvious – an enormous responsibility is taken on. The more subtle stresses are also described in this chapter. They include the necessity of the healer suppressing his own feelings, responding appropriately to the patient's feelings and those of relatives, going on caring after compassion fatigue has set in, and concealing any uncertainty he may feel.

Here a conflict between medical ethics and pleasing the patient is described:

. . . an old lady who had come to Dr J. faithfully, twice a year, for twenty years or more. When admitted to the inner sanctum, she never gave the doctor a chance to say even 'How do you do?' She burst into the room with a 'Now, doctor – don't move. I don't want you to examine me. Don't ask me any questions. Just write me a prescription for that brown tonic you gave me last year.' She always got it, paid her money and went out satisfied. Another . . . he dismissed one day, after a short conversation and a look at her tongue, saying: 'Don't worry, my dear. You will be all right. Just keep your bowels open and always wear mauve.'

. . . I never got over the fear that if I didn't go into every possibility I might be overlooking some hidden danger that hung over my patient's unsuspecting head. Hans Zinsser (1940)

A healer must be able to love and to be self-sacrificing:

The world has long since decided that you have no working hours that anyone is bound to respect, and nothing except extreme bodily illness will excuse you in its eyes from refusing to help a man who thinks he may need your help at any hour of the day or night. Nobody will care whether you are in your bed or in your bath, or on your holiday or at the theatre. Rudyard Kipling

In the room a woman moves. She is dressed in white. Lovingly she measures his hourly flow of urine . . . The man of letters did not know this woman before . . . But this nurse is his wife in his new life of dying. They are close, these two, intimate, depending one upon the other, loving. It is a marriage, for although they own no shared past, they possess this awful, intense present, this matrimonial now, that binds them as strongly as any promise. Richard Selzer (1981)

A [doctor is] a sort of nondescript creature on two legs, something between a man and an Angel. Jane Austen (1818)

In illness the physician is a father; in convalescence, a friend; when health is restored, he is a guardian. Brahmanic saying

The doctor must of course maintain professional detachment:

After this I was more on my guard than ever. I accepted her challenge, and during the weeks that followed I countered her ingenious tactics for my seduction with an unshakeably decorous professional manner. But I knew I had lost ground in that scene with the bathing costume. It is vital for a doctor to preserve at all times that indefinable barrier between himself and his patients which acts on his behalf as an amulet against temptation and, in theirs, as a sort of filtering medium which eliminates from every phase of their relations anything which might otherwise arouse self-consciousness and restraint. Harold Dearden (1940)

The doctor must also be able to see through the patient's deceits:
'She's got a terrible cough and she vomits all the time.'
The usual semantic quiz ensued. 'Has she been sick?'
'No.'
'Has she thrown up?'
'No.'
'Then what do you mean by vomiting?'
'She vomits all the time,' said Lottie firmly. She knew that Gatwood took vomiting more seriously than cough or catarrh, and therefore used the word freely as a sort of exclamation mark, to lay stress on the need for powerful drugs.

Assured that vomiting had not in fact occurred, he proceeded to carry out his routine examination of ears, chest, nose and throat. 'I can't find anything wrong with her apart from her usual dirty nose. How bad really is this cough?'

Automatically: 'It fetches her to the floor.' As the result of repeated exchanges of symptoms in the waiting-room, regular attenders eventually arrived at a stereotyped uniformity in expressing their superlatives, and could be differentiated from the genuine sick on this basis alone. Philip Auld (1959)

Living Up to Expectations

To fill the role perfectly, rather than just get by, is difficult:
To write prescriptions is easy, but to come to an understanding with people is hard. Franz Kafka (1992)

Members of the medical profession are generally portrayed as helping, caring individuals who possess almost mystical knowledge concerning the vital issues of health and sickness. They are consulted during vulnerable periods in a person's life and offer hope for relief of pain and anxiety. Adding to their godlike stature are their powers of diagnosis and healing, which can appear to be virtually miraculous to a patient frightened by the mysteries of his or her own body. Carla Fine (1981)

Healers are not normal human beings:
'We were sitting in an elegant French restaurant, celebrating our

twentieth anniversary, when the maître d' suddenly approached our table,' recounts the wife of a Chicago cardiologist. 'He whispered something to my husband, who immediately left the table and hurried into the ladies' room. The waiter looked puzzled, so I told him, "That's OK. My husband's not a man – he's a doctor."' Carla Fine (1981)

Patients expect their healers to be superhuman:

Few ways of life were hidden from Physician, and he was oftener in its darkest places than even Bishop. There were brilliant ladies about London who perfectly doted on him, my dear, as the most charming creature and the most delightful person, who would have been shocked to find themselves so close to him if they could have known on what sights those thoughtful eyes of his had rested within an hour or two, and near to whose beds, and under what roofs, his composed figure had stood. But, Physician was a composed man, who performed neither on his own trumpet, nor on the trumpets of other people. Many wonderful things did he see and hear, and much irreconcilable moral contradiction did he pass his life among; yet his equality of compassion was no more disturbed than the Divine Master's of all healing was. He went like the rain, among the just and the unjust, doing all the good he could, and neither proclaiming it in the synagogues nor at the corner of streets. Charles Dickens (1857)

Fulfilment and Affirmation for the Healer

Quite legitimately, the healer as well as the patient gains something from the partnership against disease:

I have only just resolved to become a doctor myself, having felt in one stroke – very powerfully – the contradiction between the fragility of man and the greatness of nature, together with the mystery of your dedication. Somehow, in the way you cared for these pathetic human beings I sensed an inexplicable bridge between the universe and our little selves. I sensed that if I could do what you do, I could become a conscious part of the whole greatness of nature itself. Jacob Needleman (1992)

Sometimes it is wise to accept even undeserved recognition. This is good for the healer's reputation, which perhaps enhances the effectiveness of the prescriptions. Here the writer is recounting the story of his father's first days in practice:

It was not always easy to be honest, he said. One of his first patients, who had come to see him in his new office when he was an unknown man in town, was a man complaining of grossly bloody urine. My father examined him at length, took a sample of the flawed urine, did a few other tests, and found himself without a diagnosis. To buy time enough to read up on the matter, he gave the patient a bottle of Blawd's pills, a popular iron remedy for anaemia at the time, and told him to come back to the office in four days. The patient returned on the appointed day jubilant, carrying a cask of crystal-clear urine, totally cured. In the following months my father discovered that his reputation had been made by that therapeutic triumph. Lewis Thomas (1985)

Healers often occupy a place already prepared for them in the mind of the patient:

The great physician is nothing other than the symbol of the sage, the blending of pragmatic action in the external world and conscious devotion to the Higher. Jacob Needleman (1992)

The healer needs his or her patients: they are the healer's fascination and fulfilment:

If any kind of screwball at all comes to the door, the explorer in me is awakened, my curiosity, my spirit of adventure, my sympathy. It touches my heart which is too soft . . . and I enjoy seeing what can be done with such a crazy fellow. I have made a game of healing even difficult cases. C. G. Jung (1966a)

They fall from taxis dislocating hips,
trip over paving stones in Oxford Street,
crack elbows at the theatre climbing steps,
break legs in lifts, smash ankles, damage feet.
Cheerful, alert and brave, the blue-haired grannies
phone up their transatlantic distant kin;
they order Fortnum hampers, TVs, trannies,
all week we watch their dearest friends jet in.
We picture hospitals in Hollywood

hygienic, mega-modern private suites
and wonder what they make of stodgy food
and cut-backs, dingy lighting, threadbare sheets.
But when they praise the NHS in loud
approving voices, suddenly we're proud.
Cicely Herbert (1992)

The sick man is the garden of the physicians. Swahili proverb

The Personal Qualities of the Healer

He had a peculiar way of smacking his lips and saying 'Ah!' at intervals while patients detailed their symptoms which inspired great confidence. Charles Dickens (1844)

The story below reminds us of the importance of the healer's self-control – of the ability to love, or at least accept others, however difficult that may be:

I read a story recently . . . about a chiropractor who had an opportunity to change a patient's life. One day a man who was an utter mess came into his office. The chiropractor was repelled by the man, but because he had been taught (by Indian healers, in fact) to find something lovable in each of his patients, he looked him over, searching for something he could appreciate. He saw that the man had new and very neatly tied shoelaces, so he got himself to relate to the man through his shoelaces and treated him in a loving way.

A few days later the man came back to his office, clean, well dressed, and looking much better, and he explained that on the day of his previous visit he had been headed to a nearby bridge to commit suicide when he decided he would give one more person a chance to change his mind. 'The first place I saw was your office, and so I came to you. I must thank you for being so kind to me. I felt your acceptance and your love. You encouraged me to continue living, doctor, and I want you to know what a difference your kindness made.' Bernie S. Siegel (1993)

On the other hand the repulsive part can be fascinating:

Ugliness is a point of view; an ulcer is wonderful to a pathologist.
Austin O'Malley

> . . . some men of science, osteologists
> And surgeons, beat some poets, in respect
> For nature, – count naught common or unclean,
> Spend raptures upon perfect specimens
> Of indurated veins, distorted joints,
> Or beautiful new cases of curved spine.
> Elizabeth Barrett Browning (1856)

Here the qualities that make a good surgeon are described by the man who was doctor to the Elephant Man. He wrote the book which later became the film of that name, was Edward VII's surgeon and founded the British Red Cross Society:

He must know the human body as a forester knows his wood; must know it even better than he must know the roots and branches of every tree, the source and wanderings of every rivulet, the banks of every alley, the flowers of every glade. As a surgeon, moreover, he must be learned in the moods and troubles of the wood, must know of the wild winds that may rend it, of the savage things that may lurk in its secret haunts, of the strangling creepers that may throttle its sturdiest growth, of the rot and mould that may make dust of its very heart. Sir Frederick Treves (1883)

Plato gives us a description of the ideal healer – someone who has achieved great wisdom:

And this is what the physician has to do, and in this the art of medicine consists: for medicine may be regarded generally as the knowledge of the loves and desires of the body, and how to satisfy them or not; and the best physician is he who is able to separate fair love from foul, or to convert one into the other; and he who knows how to eradicate and how to implant love, whichever is required, and can reconcile the most hostile elements in the constitution and make them loving friends, is a skilful practitioner. Plato (1995)

The ideal healer combines qualities which can rarely be found all together in one person. Professional roles tend to separate them: the doctor makes decisions, the nurse does the caring. The former has to use his head, the latter gives from the heart:

I saw that the medical mind requires a harmonic balance of thought, feeling, and instinct. This balance of three factors in the mind of man is what results in medical virtue, which of course is one expression of human virtue as such, or moral power. Out of the blend of thought, feeling, and instinct there arises authentic intuition, courage, and will, all of which, taken together, may be given the ancient name *intelligence*, a word used to great effect by the great Pythagoras and his follower Socrates, and traces of which may be discerned in one or two places in the surviving medical writings of the ancient Greeks.

Today, however, the physician is obliged only to think and decide, the nurse is obliged only to feel and clean up, and the intern is often obliged only to monitor and perform day-to-day procedures. Jacob Needleman (1992)

Sometimes quite simple and mundane things can be healing:

My favourite cleaner's from the Philippines
and cheerful too, a bonus before rounds.
Her mop seeks spots where dirt's not yet been seen
in calm broad sweeps that soothe with swishing sounds.
Cicely Herbert (1992)

15

The Healer's Burden

I spin my web
I go my rounds.
Jill Thomas (1979)

Surgeons must be very careful
When they take up the knife.
Underneath their fine incisions
Stirs the culprit – life!
Emily Dickinson (1983)

Bearing the Burden

What are the day-to-day duties of a healer?

The telephone rang. You answered it without a moment's hesitation and in that same voice spoke reassuringly to a patient at the other end of the line. I heard you using phrases that had always meant so much to me, that had always helped me so much. Jacob Needleman (1992)

He must put aside his own moods and problems and be compassionate and reassuring, and convincing about it, on demand:

Quiet, Cerebus! Soon enough you'll have a bone
or two. Now, coughing, the patient expects
the unjudged lie: 'Your symptoms are familiar
and benign' – someone to be cheerfully sure,
to transform tremblings, gigantic unease,

139

by naming like a pet some small disease
with a known aetiology, certain cure.
Dannie Abse (1989)

The skills and powers required to fill the role are not always inborn, nor do they appear automatically. They are summoned from within in a crisis:

Two burning fires of love
Looked up at me from sunken sockets,
Poured from white pillows,
So unexpected
That I, a nearly-new nurse
In pink uniform, was taken off guard,
Knocked sideways
Until swelling love
Welling inside me corrected the wobble:
I hoped my eyes answered
Oh how I hoped!
The optic messengers of this middle-aged man
Last year in his prime
Now a see-through of bones.
Looking back thirty years
I still hope my eyes answered sufficiently,
Recorded the innermost 'me',
Showing I understood what he was trying to say:
Cancer had killed his words,
I, a shy inarticulate girl,
Had not yet given birth to mine.

Instinct made me clasp skeleton hand,
Kiss the pale brow,
Surprisingly strong the fierce grasp
Of one so near death:
Did he sense I wonder
That for me
He was the turning-point?

From then on I loved people;
I hope.
Margaret Gillies (1979)

Walt Whitman volunteered to work in the ambulance corps:

I dress a wound in the side, deep, deep, deep,
But a day or two more, for see the frame all wasted and sinking,
And the yellow-blue countenance see.

I dress the perforated shoulder, the foot with the bullet wound,
Cleanse the one with a gnawing and putrid gangrene, so sickening,
    so offensive,
While the attendant stands behind aside holding the tray and
    pail.

I am faithful, I do not give out,
The fractured thigh, the knee, the wound in the abdomen,
These and more I dress with impassive hand (yet deep in my
    breast a fire, a burning flame).
Walt Whitman (1865)

Attachments between Healer and Healed

A professional healer has to develop 'transferable love'. This love goes from patient to patient, according to need. When patients get better they are no longer the centre of attention:

One particular memory, of all my hospital memories, many grue-some, sticks with me. It was late on the second night after my operation; I was attempting to be sick on a totally empty stomach, irrationally convinced that I would tear my stitches apart; and in the dim light three beautiful young nurses, all looking as though they were the ghosts of 'stunners' painted by Rossetti a century ago, were attempting to support and calm me. 'Take it easy ... It's all right ... That's it ...' Most of us, if we had to minister to an old codger while he was attempting to bring up his guts, would show some distaste, as well as concern. There was no distaste whatever, only a patient tenderness, on the faces around me.

The sadness comes when one realizes the tenderness is not something personal, a tribute to some quality within oneself, but merely professional. As one gets better so inevitably the manner of one's nurses – now concerned with other patients in crisis – becomes brisker, more peremptory. One's temperature is taken once a day, one's blood pressure ceases to be taken. A head appears around a door. 'Everything all right, Mr King?' 'Yes, thank you.' 'Well, don't hesitate to ring if you want anything.' The head disappears. Francis King (1988)

The healer is the centre of a whole network of caring connections, like a guardian angel with many charges. This poem was written by a night-nurse in a home for blind children:

> Swinging out over the hinterland
> of other's sleep
> I spiral round
>
> on silken thread of duty.
> Spider-like
> in my solitary
>
> watchfulness I gather the lines of care,
> brooding over
> their trusting sleep. Their
>
> unknown dreaming lands.
> I spin my web
> I go my rounds.
> Jill Thomas (1979)

Two ways in which a healer might be tempted to go too far are described below:

I have always had a sneaking liking for lunatics. I used to wander about quite unconcerned in the Salle des Agités as among friends. I had been warned more than once that it would end badly, but of course I knew better. One day, one of my best friends hit me on the back of the head with a hammer he got hold of in some inexplicable way, and I was carried unconscious to the infirmary. It was a terrible blow, my friend was an ex-blacksmith who knew his business. Axel Munthe (1949)

Keep up the spirits of your patient with the music of the viol and the psaltery, or by forging letters telling of the death of his enemies or (if he be a cleric) by informing him that he has been made a bishop. Henri de Mondeville

The Healer's Rewards

The sage, in velvet chair, here lolls at ease,
To promise future health for present fees.
Sir Samuel Garth (1699)

The next piece of writing raises questions about financial rewards for the healing professions:

Doctors should walk about like sages honoured and protected by all men. They should be welcome to take what they liked from their rich patients for their poor patients and themselves, but they should not count their visits or write any bills. What was to the heart of the mother the value in cash of the life of the child you had saved? What was the proper fee for taking the fear of death out of the terror-stricken eyes by a comforting word or a mere stroke of your hand? How many francs were you to charge for every second of the death struggle your morphia syringe had snatched from the executioner? How long were we to dump on suffering mankind all these expensive patent medicines and drugs with modern labels but with roots in medieval superstition? We well know that our number of efficacious drugs could be counted on the ends of our fingers and were handed to us by benevolent Mother Nature at a cheap price. Why should I, who was a fashionable doctor, drive about in a smart carriage, while my colleague in the slums had to walk about on foot? Why did the state spend many hundred times more money on teaching the art of killing than the art of healing? Axel Munthe (1949)

The profession has privileges and rewards other than financial:

One can have the exclusive scientific life that touches the distances, and befriend the old fogies in the parish too. George Eliot (1871–2)

The doctor . . . really has an acquaintance with us as we are, who is admitted to some of us every day with our wigs and paint off, who hears the wanderings of our minds, and sees the undisguised expressions of our faces. Charles Dickens (1857)

The realities of human nature are clear in illness, and secrets are revealed to medical practitioners. Somerset Maugham reflects on his medical training:

I have reasons for believing that the training a medical student has to go through is to a writer's benefit . . . When people are ill, when they are afraid, they discard the mask which they wear in health. The doctor sees them as they really are, selfish, hard, grasping, cowardly; but brave, too, generous, kindly and good. He is tolerant of their frailties, awed by their virtues. Somerset Maugham (1959)

One is allowed into 'the secret gardens of the self' and something magical can happen there:

My 'medicine' was the thing which gained me entrance to . . . the secret gardens of the self. It lay there, another world, in the self. I was permitted by my medical badge to follow the poor, defeated body into those gulfs and grottoes. And the astonishing thing is that at such time and in such places – foul as they may be with the stinking ischiorectal abscesses of our comings and goings – just there, the thing, in all its greatest beauty, may be freed for a moment to fly guiltily around the room. William Carlos Williams (1967)

The healer may reach a new understanding:

He stumbled from the night
of drums and cicadas
into the lamp lit gloom
of a doctor's waiting room . . .
a Bantu boy of twelve
groping, bumping into chairs.
'What's wrong?' I said. 'My eyes,'
he panted; 'a snake
spat poison at me; now
I'm blind, I see nothing.'
He was trembling, still afraid,
on edge, as if expecting

some further blow, perhaps
the winding up of a spell.

On the examining couch
he lay supine and heard
my quiet words . . .
                            and blinked
when my clenched fist
flashed close to his blank face.
'Did you see that?' 'See what?'
he asked, with innocence.
I murmured to myself
'Hysteria,' and smiled,
believing now that one
might cure him of his blindness.

'Keep your eyes closed
while I count up to ten:
then open them and you will see':
those words from my open mouth . . .
strange as an oracle!
I counted solemnly,
half dreading to reach 'ten'.
How could such magic work,
when all that I had done
was diagnose, and talk?

'Ten: open your eyes.'
He opened and cried out
'I see! I see!'
And as I touched his brow
it seemed an unsuspected power
had passed through my bones
to him – in a blinding
but sight-restoring spark that gave
new sight also to me.

Edward Lowbury (1968)

The Need to Heal

The role of healer can be a refuge for a troubled soul – one is so busy with the troubles of others there is no need to face one's own:

He imagined himself as a sort of mobile one-man hospital. He performed appendix and hernia operations on kitchen tables.

. . . He dealt only with crises in which he was the central character: or, to put it another way, in which the patient was *simplified* by the degree of his physical dependence on the doctor. He was also simplified himself, because the chosen pace of his life made it impossible and unnecessary for him to examine his own motives. John Berger and Jean Mohr (1967)

One can lose oneself in other people's problems:

But the actual calling on people, at all times and under all conditions, the coming to grips with the intimate conditions of their lives, when they were being born, when they were dying, watching them die, watching them get well when they were ill, has always absorbed me. I lost myself in the very properties of their minds: for the moment at least I actually became *them*, whoever they should be, so that when I detached myself from them at the end of a half hour of intense concentration over some illness which was affecting them, it was as though I were reawakening from a sleep. For a moment I myself did not exist; nothing of myself affected me. As a consequence I came back to myself, as from any other sleep, rested. William Carlos Williams (1967)

Or one can find oneself in the relationship with a patient:

'There's nothing like a difficult patient to show us ourselves,' Williams once said to a medical student, and then he expanded the observation: 'I felt like a thief because I heard words, lines, saw people and places – and used it all in my writing. I guess I've told people that, and no one's so surprised! There was something deeper going on, though – the *force* of all those encounters. I was put off guard again and again, and the result was – well, a descent into myself.' Robert Coles, in introduction to William Carlos Williams (1984)

The Sacrifice

He went home and read far into the smallest hour, bringing a much more testing vision of details and relations into his pathological study than he had ever thought it necessary to apply to the complexities of love and marriage. George Eliot (1871–2)

The next piece concerns the fourth wise man, a figure who is not mentioned in the Bible story of Christ's birth. He is faced with a terrible dilemma on his journey to join the other three:

The dim starlight revealed the form of a man lying across the road. His humble dress and the outline of his haggard face showed that he was probably one of the poor Hebrew exiles who still dwelt in great numbers in the vicinity. His pallid skin, dry and yellow as parchment, bore the mark of the deadly fever which ravaged the marshlands in autumn. The chill of death was in his lean hand, and, as Artaban released it, the arm fell back inertly upon the motionless breast.

He turned away with a thought of pity, consigning the body to that strange burial which the Magians deemed most fitting – the funeral of the desert, from which the kites and vultures rise on dark wings, and the beasts of prey slink furtively away, leaving only a heap of white bones in the sand.

But, as he turned, a long, faint, ghostly sigh came from the man's lips. The brown, bony fingers closed convulsively on the hem of the Magian's robe and held him fast.

Artaban's heart leaped to his throat, not with fear, but with a dumb resentment at the importunity of this blind delay.

How could he stay here in the darkness to minister to a dying stranger? What claim had this unknown fragment of human life upon his compassion or his service? If he lingered but for an hour he could hardly reach Borsippa at the appointed time. His companions would think he had given up the journey. They would go without him. He would lose his quest.

But if he went on now, the man would surely die. If he stayed, life might be restored. His spirit throbbed and fluttered with the urgency of the crisis. Should he risk the great reward of his divine faith for the sake of a single deed of human love? Should he turn aside, if only for a moment, from the following of the star, to give a cup of cold water to a poor, perishing Hebrew?

'God of truth and purity,' he prayed, 'direct me in the holy path, the way of wisdom which Thou only knowest.'

Then he turned back to the sick man. Loosening the grasp of his hand, he carried him to a little mound at the foot of the palm tree.

He unbound the thick folds of the turban and opened the garment above the sunken breast. He brought water from one of the small canals near by, and moistened the sufferer's brow and mouth. He mingled a draught of one of those simple but potent remedies which he carried always in his girdle – for the Magians were physicians as well as astrologers – and poured it slowly between the colourless lips. Hour after hour he laboured as only a skilful healer of disease can do; and, at last, the man's strength returned; he sat up and looked about him.

'Who art thou?' he said, in the rude dialect of the country, 'and why hast thou sought me here to bring back my life?'

'I am Artaban the Magian, of the city of Ecbatana, and I am going to Jerusalem in search of one who is to be born King of the Jews, a great Prince and Deliverer of all men. I dare not delay any longer upon my journey, for the caravan that has waited for me may depart without me. But see, here is all that I have left of bread and wine, and here is a potion of healing herbs. When thy strength is restored thou canst find the dwellings of the Hebrews among the houses of Babylon.'

The Jew raised his trembling hand solemnly to heaven.

'Now may the God of Abraham and Isaac and Jacob bless and prosper the journey of the merciful, and bring him in peace to his desired haven. But stay; I have nothing to give thee in return – only this: that I can tell thee where the messiah must be sought. For our prophets have said that he should be born, not in Jerusalem, but in Bethlehem of Judah. May the Lord bring thee in safety to that place, because thou hast had pity upon the sick.' Henry van Dyke (1905)

The fourth wise man eventually finds his own destiny in humble service to the poor and unfortunate. Mother Teresa said that 'we can see Christ in the broken bodies of the poor'.

16

The Heroic Healer and the Wounded Healer

Today, the physician contends alone with life and death, because the gods are dead – or so he believes. James Hillman (1964)

The Heroic Healer

I haven't got time to be sick . . . people need me. Don Marquis (1946)

The role of healer can be empowering:

In this man, so insignificant, so common, there was, in these brief moments in which he deliberated, in which the relative dangers of one and another course of treatment presented themselves alternately to his mind until he came to a decision, the same sort of greatness as in a general . . . Marcel Proust (1995)

On the basis of this the healer can become a hero:

Upon the occasion of my first visit to Rome I completely won the admiration of the philosopher Glaucon by the diagnosis which I made in the case of one of his friends. Meeting me one day in the street he shook hands with me and said: 'I have just come from the house of a sick man, and I wish that you would visit him with me. He is a Sicilian physician, the same person with whom I was walking when you met me the other day.'

'What is the matter with him?' I asked.

Then coming nearer to me he said, in the frankest manner possible: 'Giorgias and Apelas told me yesterday that you had made some diagnoses and prognoses which looked to them more like acts of divination than products of the medical art pure and simple. I would therefore like very much to see some proof, not of your knowledge, but of this extraordinary art which you are said to possess.'

At this very moment we reached the entrance of the patient's house, and so, to my regret, I was prevented from having any further conversation with him on the subject and from explaining to him how the element of good luck often renders it possible for a physician to give, as it were offhand, diagnoses and prognoses of this exceptional character. Just as we were approaching the first door, after entering the house, we met a servant who had in his hand a basin which he had brought from the sickroom and which he was on his way to empty upon the dung heap. As we passed him I appeared not to pay any attention to the contents of the basin, but at a mere glance I perceived that they consisted of a thin sanio-sanguinolent fluid, in which floated excrementitious masses that resembled shreds of flesh – an unmistakable evidence of disease of the liver. Glaucon and I, not a word having been spoken by either of us, passed on into the patient's room. When I put out my hand to feel the latter's pulse, he called my attention to the fact that he had just had a stool, and that, owing to the circumstances of his having gotten out of bed, his pulse might be accelerated. It was in fact somewhat more rapid than it should be, but I attributed this to the existence of an inflammation. Then, observing upon the window-sill a vessel containing a mixture of hyssop and honey and water, I made up my mind that the patient, who was a physician, believed that the malady from which he was suffering was a pleurisy, the pain which he experienced on the right side in the region of the false ribs (and which is also associated with inflammation of the liver) confirming him in his belief, and thus inducing him to order for the relief of the slight accompanying cough the mixture to which I have called attention. It was then that the idea came to my mind that, as fortune had thrown the opportunity in my way, I would avail myself of the opportunity to enhance my reputation in Glaucon's estimation.

Accordingly, placing my hand on the patient's right side over the false rib, I remarked: 'This is the spot where the disease is located.'

He, supposing that I must have gained this knowledge by feeling his pulse, replied with a look which plainly expressed admiration mingled with astonishment, that I was entirely right.

'And,' I added simply to increase his astonishment, 'you will doubtless admit that at long intervals you feel impelled to indulge in a shallow, dry cough, unaccompanied by any expectoration.'

As luck would have it, he coughed in just this manner almost before I had got the words out of my mouth. At this Glaucon, who had hitherto not spoken a word, broke out into a volley of praises.

'Do not imagine,' I replied, 'that what you have observed represents the utmost of which the medical art is capable in the matter of fathoming the mysteries of disease in a living person. There still remain one or two other symptoms to which I will direct your attention.'

Turning then to the patient I remarked: 'When you draw a longer breath you feel a more marked pain, do you not, in the region which I indicated; and with this pain there is associated a sense of weight in the hypochondrium?'

At these words the patient expressed his astonishment and admiration in the strongest possible terms. I wanted to go a step further and announce to my audience still another symptom which is sometimes observed in the more serious maladies of the liver (schirrus, for example), but I was afraid that I might compromise the laudation which had been bestowed upon me. It then occurred to me that I might safely make this announcement if I put it somewhat in the form of a prognosis.

So I remarked to the patient: 'You will probably soon experience, if you have not already done so, a sensation of something pulling on the right clavicle.'

He admitted that he had already noticed this symptom.

'Then I will give you just one more evidence of the powers of divination which you believe that I possess. You, yourself, before I arrived on the scene, had made up your mind that your ailment was an attack of pleurisy, etc.'

Glaucon's confidence in me and in the medical art, after this episode, was unbounded. Galen

A variation on this theme is the heroic healer who becomes angry with God for allowing suffering:

If a man looks with loving compassion on his suffering fellow men and out of his bitterness inquires of the gods, 'Why do you afflict my brothers?' then he is gazed upon more tenderly by God than a man who congratulates him on being merciful so that he flourishes happily,

THE SOUL OF MEDICINE

and has only words of adoration to offer. For the first prays out of love and pity, divine attributes, and so is close to the heart of God, and the other speaks out of selfish complacency, a beastly attribute, which does not approach the circumambient light of the spirit of God. Horace

Such a healer is described below. A mother has died in childbirth and the baby is dead too:

'Live!' Lucanus commanded the child, and great drops of sweat poured from his flesh and drenched his garments. And his strong breath went in and out of the throat of the infant, like life itself, grim and purposeful, not to be denied. His fingers gently but firmly circled the child's chest, compressing then quickly relieving as he held the little one against his heart with his left hand and arm, and breathed steadily into its throat.

. . . he poured his breath and his will and his life into the infinitesimal body. The child stirred against his heart, fragilely, like a struggling bird. Its bloodstained face lost its pallor, flushed deeply. One hand, unbelievably minute, thrust against the woollen rug.

'It lives!' cried Keptah, overcome with joy. 'It breathes! It is a miracle from God!' Taylor Caldwell (1959)

Later, in a ship where the plague has broken out among the slaves rowing in the galleys, he himself becomes god-like:

He stood among the wrack of the ill, the dying and the dead, and to Cusa he did indeed have the aspect of a conquering God. He had hung the lantern on a hook in the oozing ceiling. His garments were stained with blood and corruption. But his face was a radiance. Taylor Caldwell (1959)

The healer-hero is the opponent of death, and fights alone:

The prime carrier of the death-fighter image today is the physician. The principle of consciousness, of light and air and sky, has been materialized into his gleaming surgical and rainbow-hued pharmaceutical instruments . . . the battle against the regressive dragon of unconsciousness, the 'jaws of death', is repeated every time the physician splints and bandages or writes a prescription. Therefore the physician must treat. Above all else *he must do something*. James Hillman (1964)

Seeing oneself in this way can be inspiring:

My own conception of the job has been to consider myself a man in the front line, in the trenches. It's the only way I can respect myself and go on treating what comes, men, women and children. William Carlos Williams (1967)

This military analogy can be abused, and there are dangers in the heroic healer role:

Too often we view ourselves as medical soldiers of a sort, waging war against disease ... Of course reality is very different. Illness always occurs in the *context* of a person's life. The setting in which illness emerges has much to do with a person's life – his relationships, work, setbacks, triumphs, hopes, defeats, dreams, and struggles.

What does such a perspective do, for example, to the doctor–patient relationship? The answer has to be a great deal of harm ... [The patient becomes] a fragile boat, a rudderless frigate, a hapless barge of statistical misfortune tossed upon the stormy seas of illness. The doctor in turn views his responsibilities as a naval skirmish – a confrontation to be prepared for, fought, and won ... Viewing medicine as a battle too often reduces the patient to an object ...

We speak of *combating* an infection. We *attack* the problem of heart disease. We try to *conquer* cancer. In short medicine is a battle. It is war. Disease is an evil invader that has landed on the patient's shores from some remote and barbarous region. When the patient begins to lose the battle against this invader he calls the doctor in. Like a hired gunslinger or Samurai warrior, the doctor takes up the fray.

... The patient in this perspective is entirely passive. He hopes only to be saved. The doctor sends in his armada and tries to occupy disease's strategic islands; or occasionally he has to retreat. What he does not do is relate well to his patient. David Reiser and David Rosen (1984)

Burn-out

When you have to exhaust yourself terribly for a person and you don't get paid for it, in time you lose your taste for it. C. G. Jung

'All right, let's get started.' He pressed the buzzer on the desk to summon his first patient. The door facing him opened to admit a young mother with four young children. Mrs Pearce handed him five record envelopes, indicating that all five required his attention. He viewed the invasion without enthusiasm. Philip Auld (1959)

What is the effect of carrying the burden of being a healer? The reliable responsiveness may be taken for granted by patients. The healer may not notice the increasing exhaustion:

As a physician, I am aware of how draining and threatening empathy for helpless, injured people can be. I know how hard it is to hold on to compassion when all of one's invested power and energy seems helpless against the tide of fate . . . As a patient, I felt more alone, more helpless, more terrified, and more enraged than I now believe I had to be. Judith Alexander Brice (1987)

The healer has to carry on somehow:

No recourse was left to him but to tighten the stranglehold on his feelings and harden his heart protectively. For he knew this was the only way of carrying on. In any case, he had few illusions left, and fatigue was robbing him of even those remaining few. He knew that, over a period whose end he could not glimpse, his task was no longer to cure, but to diagnose. Albert Camus (1995)

The Healer in Despair

And thus I dreamt that round me stood
The victims of disease,
The patients I had failed to cure,
Though some had paid my fees.
William Snowdon Battles

Here is an acute episode of therapeutic desperation. While attending a difficult birth out in the wilds without equipment or support, the healer casts around for help where no help can be found:

A quiet hiss came through clenched teeth in soft bursts. A swatch of black hair escaped upon the table, and through its filigree one could see the characters of the Korean newspaper spread beneath her body. Sloane stared at the newsprint as if it were a coded message from some ancient oriental midwife who had fathomed the secrets of childbirth in this land, and who had plied her trade through quiet centuries in a manner leathery, silent, and brave. If he could but read from those characters her fearless instructions, he would have it then, the way to save these two – not even that; the way to endure it with them. Richard Selzer (1974)

In such circumstances the healer may be ready to resort to unusual methods:

Experience has proved the toad to be endowed with valuable qualities. If you run a stick through three toads, and, after having dried them in the sun, apply them to any pestilent tumour, they draw out all the poison, and the malady will disappear. Martin Luther

> I remember the night my mother
> was stung by a scorpion . . .
> my mother twisted through and through
> groaning on a mat,
> my father, sceptic, rationalist,
> trying every curse and blessing,
> powder, mixture herb and hybrid.
> He even poured a little paraffin
> upon the bitten toe and put a match to it.
>
> Nissim Ezekiel (1982)

At our most pernicious and desperate, we fall back on magic and mumbo-jumbo to help us rewrite a reality we cannot bear to face. We turn to crystals, prayer, Japanese herbs, macrobiotic diets, the worship of idols or vitamin pills, to defeat the cellular rebellion within our own bodies of cancerous cells or the blind immoral onslaught of the HIV virus. Sometimes, understandably, we even turn to textbooks, science, as if the knowledge of an overwhelming enemy was enough in itself to defeat its power. Kevin Toolis (1996)

Medicine may be defined as the art of keeping a patient quiet . . . until nature kills him or cures him. Gilles Menage (1650)

Self-doubt

The healer is desperate to help, but the answer will not come.

My patient kept getting worse. You are not a doctor, my good sir; you cannot understand what passes in a poor fellow's heart, especially at first, when he begins to suspect that the disease is getting the upper hand of him. What becomes of his belief in himself? You suddenly grow so timid; it's indescribable. You fancy then that you have forgotten everything you knew, and that the patient has no faith in you, and that other people begin to notice how distracted you are, and tell you the symptoms with reluctance; that they are looking at you suspiciously, whispering . . . Ah! it's horrid! There must be a remedy, you think, for this disease, if one could find it. Isn't this it? You try – no, that's not it! You don't allow the medicine the necessary time to do good . . . You clutch at one thing, then at another. Sometimes you take up a book of medical prescriptions – here it is, you think! Sometimes, by Jove, you pick one out by chance, thinking to leave it to fate . . . But meantime a fellow creature's dying, and another doctor would have saved him . . . But what's still more torture to you is to see blind faith in you, and to feel yourself that you are not able to be of use. Ivan Turgenev (1974)

In the next piece the healer is too ill to concentrate on his patients:

I did not go off my head, I did not kill myself. I staggered on with my work as best I could, careless, indifferent to what happened to myself, and what happened to my patients. Beware of a doctor who suffers from insomnia! My patients began to complain that I was rough and impatient with them, many of them left me, many stuck to me still and so much the worse for them. Only when they were about to die did I seem to wake up from my torpor, for I continued to take keen interest in Death long after I had lost all interest in Life. Axel Munthe (1949)

Here the healer is at the end of his tether.

To hell with them all . . . to hell . . . They think I am a doctor, I am able to cure every kind of illness, but I know absolutely nothing at all, I've forgotten everything I knew, I remember nothing, absolutely nothing at all . . . Last Wednesday I treated a woman . . . she died and it's my fault she died . . . I knew something or other twenty-five years ago, but now I remember nothing at all. Anton Chekhov (1977)

Full Circle: The Healer Becomes the Patient

A physician often cannot heal the people closest to himself or herself:

And he said unto them, Ye will surely say unto me this proverb, Physician heal thyself: whatsoever we have heard done in Capernaum, do also here in thy country. And he said, Verily I say unto you, No prophet is accepted in his own country. Luke iv, 23

Nor can healers truly heal themselves. Now we have come full circle. The healer has neglected the patient within himself or herself, and has been overcome by his or her own sickness. The healer now has to become a patient.

No man is a good physician who has never been sick. Arabic proverb

> Not till you play the patient in your turn,
> The morning visit's mystery shall you learn.
> Oliver Wendell Holmes

To be ill, or to undergo an operation, is to be initiated into the mystery of nursing, and to learn the comforts and discomforts of an invalid's life; the unearthly fragrance of tea at daybreak . . . and the behaviour of each constituent part of the bedclothes. You know, henceforth, how many hours are in a sleepless night; and what unclean fancies will not let us alone when we are ill . . . and how we cling to life, not from any terror of death, nor with any clear desire for the remainder of life, but by nature, not by logic. In brief, you learn from your own case many facts which are not in textbooks and lectures; and your patients, in the years to come, will say that they prefer you to the other doctor . . . Stephen Paget (1908)

A good healer knows what it is like to be a patient and has learned about suffering at first hand. Likewise, a good patient is not just a patient, but is also active in the healing process.

Finally, when we use whatever difficulties we have experienced to help others, then all our suffering and struggles are raised up and given purpose and dignity even beyond ourselves. They are redeemed ... The principle of sacrifice is operating whenever others learn a better way through our suffering. But it is not our suffering that is the gift. It is our healing. Spiritual development and healing are essentially the same thing. Through our suffering and healing we help to enlighten humanity as a whole. Our own personal tragedy, regarded from this perspective, precipitates a deeper comprehension of the true meaning and purpose of individual existence, intertwining our personal healing with the healing of the planet. Robin Norwood (1995)

PART II
AFFLICTIONS FROM THE CRADLE
TO THE GRAVE

17

Birth and Childhood

Birth

Our birth is but a sleep and a forgetting;
The Soul that rises with us, our life's Star,
Hath had elsewhere its setting,
And cometh from afar:
Not in entire forgetfulness,
And not in utter nakedness,
But trailing clouds of glory do we come
From God who is our home:
Heaven lies about us in our infancy!
Shades of the prison house begin to close
Upon the growing Boy,
But he beholds the light, and whence it flows,
He sees it in his joy;
The Youth, who daily farther from the east
Must travel, still is Nature's Priest,
And by the vision splendid
Is on his way attended;
At length the Man perceives it die away,
And fade into the light of common day . . .
William Wordsworth (1969)

My mother groan'd, my father wept.
Into the dangerous world I leapt:
Helpless, naked, piping loud:
Like a fiend hid in a cloud.

William Blake (1794)

From the private ease of Mother's womb
I fall into the lighted room.

Why don't they simply put me back
Where it is warm and wet and black?

But one thing follows on another.
Things were different inside Mother.

Padded and jolly I would ride
The perfect comfort of her inside.

They tuck me in a rustling bed
– I lie there, raging, small and red.

I may sleep soon, I may forget,
But I won't forget that I regret.

A rain of blood poured round her womb,
But all time roars outside this room.

Thom Gunn (1979)

For a Sick Child

Eat no green apples or you'll droop,
Be careful not to get the croup,
Avoid the chickenpox and such,
And don't fall out of windows much.

Edward Anthony (1942)

The poems in this section take a light-hearted look at illness from a child's point of view. They will appeal when the illness is not too serious and the main problem as far as the child is concerned is having to stay in bed while friends are still out playing – or having to go to school:

When I was sick and lay a-bed,
I had two pillows at my head,
And all my toys beside me lay
To keep me happy all the day.
And sometimes for an hour or so
I watched my leaden soldiers go,
With different uniforms and drills,
Among the bed-clothes, through the hills;

And sometimes sent my ships in fleets
All up and down among the sheets;
Or brought my trees and houses out,
And planted cities all about.
I was the giant great and still
That sits upon the pillow-hill,
And sees before him, dale and plain,
The pleasant land of counterpane.

Robert Louis Stevenson (1885)

'I cannot go to school today,'
Said little Peggy Ann McKay.
'I have the measles and the mumps,
A gash, a rash and purple bumps.
My mouth is wet, my throat is dry,
I'm going blind in my right eye.
My tonsils are as big as rocks,
I've counted sixteen chicken pox
And there's one more – that's seventeen,
And don't you think my face looks green?
My leg is cut, my eyes are blue –
It might be instamatic flu.
I cough and sneeze and gasp and choke,
I'm sure that my left leg is broke –'

Shel Silverstein (1984)

18

Afflictions One by One

'The Dispensary', a seventeenth-century poem, gives a fearful impression of the effects of disease. There are so many ways to suffer:

> Dim lamps with sickly rays scarce seem to glow;
> Sighs heave in mournful moans, and tears o'erflow.
> Restless Anxiety, forlorn Despair,
> And all the faded family of Care.
> Old mouldering urns, racks, daggers and distress
> Make up the frightful horror of the place.
>   Within its dreadful jaws those furies wait,
> Which execute the harsh decrees of fate.
> Febris is first: the hag relentless hears
> The virgin's sighs, and sees the infant's tears.
> In her parch'd eyeballs fiery meteors reign;
> And restless ferments revel in each vein.
>   The Hydrops next appears amongst the throng;
> Bloated, and big, she slowly sails along.
> But like a miser, in excess she's poor,
> And pines for thirst amidst her wat'ry store.
>   Now loathsome Lepra, that offensive Sprite,
> With foul eruptions stain'd, offends the sight;
> Still deaf to beauty's soft persuading pow'r;
> Nor can bright Hebe's charms her bloom secure.
>   Whilst meagre Pthisis gives a silent blow,
> Her strokes are sure, but her advances slow.
> No loud alarms or fierce assaults are shown;
> She starves the fortress first, then takes the town.

Behind stood crowds of much inferior name,
Too num'rous to repeat, too foul to name,
The vassals of their monarch's tyranny.
Who, at his nod, on fatal errands fly.

Sir Samuel Garth (1999)

This chapter includes pieces of writing on a random selection of diseases, traumas and woes of various kinds. The afflictions considered may be minor indispositions or profound sufferings. The tone of the pieces varies from humorous to deadly serious and shocking. They are in alphabetical order for ease of reference.

Addiction

My supply
of tablets
has got to last for years and years.
I like them more than I like me.
Stubborn as hell, they won't let go.
It's a kind of marriage.
It's a kind of war
where I plant bombs inside
of myself.

Anne Sexton (1967)

But it is cigarette smoke that most subtly rebuilds past moments for me . . . A mentholated cigarette, a cheap cigar can bathe in tenderness almost any moment from my past. Fernando Pessoa (1991)

One drinker recounted: 'Always we'd emerge with a new formula for avoiding future trouble. "You've got to space your drinks and take plenty of water in between" or "coat the stomach with a little olive oil", or "drink anything but those damn martinis".'

. . . 'I made promises to myself, my family and friends – and broke them.' Starhawk (1987)

The Censor stops us from revealing both our real pain and our power. The delusion that the Censor imposes is that pain will go away if we keep quiet. As long as we say nothing, as long as no one notices anything, as long as what is happening is not named, it is not real.

'Don't talk' is one of the unspoken rules in alcoholic families.

Thirteen-year-old Steve said, 'I thought I was going crazy. I thought I was the only one in the house who knew Dad was an alcoholic . . . No one else ever said anything' . . . I asked his mother and his older sister why they hadn't talked with Steve. They responded, 'Because he hadn't said anything, and we hoped he hadn't noticed.' Claudia Black (1981)

In order to knock it out of him, it is necessary to produce a revolution in all the organs and members of the body. Anton Chekhov (1960)

Asthma

But breathing . . . is not necessarily easy. It is one of those physical acts on the edge of thought; it can be conscious or unconscious. These semi-conscious acts are troublesome: start to think about your blinking, and it is hard to stop, and hard not to feel squeamish about your entire optical apparatus; consider your walking, and you tend to stiffen and stumble. John Updike (1989)

An asthma attack feels like two walls drawn closer, and closer, until they are pressed together . . . I thought, *This is the last thing I'll see. This is death.* John Updike (1989)

> I hold
> my breath
> Out of fear
> of her fear
> Of my fear
>
> And I hold
> My breath
> To hold
> Her

She is held
As she holds
Her breath
As she watches
Me hold
My breath

Now we
Understand one another
This is a sort of
Life
Together.
Alix Pirani (1978)

Bowel Problems

Twenty-two feet of wonders
Twenty-two feet of woes;
Why we're obliged to have so many yards of them
Nobody really knows.

Sometimes they lie retentive,
Sometimes they're wild and free,
Sometimes they writhe and get madly expulsive
The moment you're out to tea.
Connie Bensley (1990)

I wish I had the voice of Homer
To sing of rectal carcinoma,
Which kills a lot more chaps in fact,
Than were bumped off when Troy was sacked.

I noticed I was passing blood
(Only a few drops, not a flood)
So pausing on my homeward way
From Tallahasse to Bombay

I asked a doctor, now a friend,
To peer into my hinder end,
To prove or disprove the rumour
That I had a malignant tumour.

J. B. S. Haldane (1951)

Cancer

I discovered my lump in October. As soon as I went to the doctor with it, I was sure that something big, something important was happening . . . I knew it would be vital to keep in touch with myself, to tell myself the truth, to keep myself centred and not let myself get swamped or scattered. If I was going on a roller-coaster ride I wanted to drive, or at least sit up front so I could see what was happening: I didn't want to be dragged along behind.

I started my journal. Julie Friedberger (1996)

People with other diseases are just plain sick; those with cancer 'fight' it. During my heart trouble, no one suggested I fight my heart, but one of the first things I was told about cancer was, 'You have to fight.' Read any set of obituaries. People die of cancer after a 'valiant battle' or a 'long bout'. Government research programmes are 'wars' on cancer. Newspaper stories that refer to poverty, crime, and drug abuse as 'cancers' reflect society's attitude toward cancer as the dreaded other. Against this other, combat is the only appropriate response. But I do not believe that illness should be lived as a fight.

We thought of ourselves as civilians whose home had become a battlefield. Demands and crises followed one after the other so fast that we felt buffeted. Arthur Frank (1991)

I may have bounced back from a heart attack, but with cancer I was going to have to sink all the way through and discover a life on the other side. Arthur Frank (1991)

Most people opt for the tumour-as-alien. At the extreme, Ronald Reagan's well-known statement about his cancer, 'I don't have cancer. I had something inside of me that had cancer in it, and it was removed,' sums up this unwillingness to understand cancer as part of oneself. I only hope this served Reagan well. For myself, I had cancer. Arthur Frank (1991)

The body collapses, so that it may sweat out, if I may put it like that, the unrightful etheric processes that it has taken into itself under the Ahrimanic influence . . . In many cases it is the only means available to the powers of good if they are to save the individual from the clutches of Ahriman. [Ahriman is one aspect of evil. Ed.] Rudolf Steiner (1976)

Perhaps cancer (and I would say that the same could be said of any illness) is an experiment in the creation of greater personality, urging it on to the frontier of its existence, in order to constellate there the meaning and purpose of one's destiny previously denied. Jung said, 'It was only after my illness that I understood how important it is to affirm one's own destiny.' And it was after his illness that his most creative work was done, by his own admission. Russell Lockheart (1977)

In reality the human being is a whole and as such connected with the cosmos, and is forever involved in the struggle against the self-will of the cell. Rudolf Steiner (1981)

> Doctor Thomas sat over his dinner
> Though his wife was waiting to ring,
> Rolling his bread into pellets;
> Said, 'Cancer's a funny thing.
>
> 'Nobody knows what the cause is,
> Though some pretend they do;
> It's like some hidden assassin
> Waiting to strike at you.
>
> 'Childless women get it,
> And men when they retire;
> It's as if there had to be some outlet
> For the foiled creative fire.'
> W. H. Auden (1967)

Claustrophobia

Our lives depend upon an interior maze of pumping, oozing tubular flow whose contemplation itself can induce claustrophobia . . . how narrow are those passageways by which the ego communicates with the world. John Updike (1989)

The Common Cold

If you want a cure for a cold, put on two pullovers, take up a baton, poker or pencil, tune the radio to a symphony concert, stand on a chair, and conduct like mad for an hour or so and the cold will have vanished. It never fails. You know why conductors live so long? Because we perspire so much. Sir John Barbirolli

> The cure for this ill is not to sit still
> Or frowst with a book by the fire
> But to take a large hoe and a shovel also
> And dig till you gently perspire.
> Rudyard Kipling (1902)

In the night my cold passed from the stage of incubation to the stage of exasperation, and I woke up with weeping eyes, a streaming nose, no sense of taste, and very little sense of hearing. Went to work, kicking dogs, swearing at children, and pushing old women under buses. There is a misanthrope in every man, and the cold germ usually brings him well to the fore. Robertson Davies (1986)

Consciousness

To be too conscious is an illness. Feodor Dostoevsky (1864)

> Life is an incurable disease.
> Abraham Cowley (1656)

Man, by the very fact of being man, by possessing consciousness, is, in comparison with the ass or the crab, a diseased animal. Consciousness is a disease. Miguel de Unamuno (1967)

The world, of which my fiancée is a representative, and my self shatter my body in an irreconcilable contrast. Franz Kafka (0000)

The true believer is in a high degree protected against the danger of certain neurotic afflictions; by accepting the universal neurosis he is spared the task of forming a personal neurosis. Sigmund Freud (1962)

Constipation

But Joe was . . . the blustering cuckoo in our nest. He would return from the bathroom announcing the state of his bowels in fake tabloid headlines – *The Big Shit, Joe's Monster Turd* or *Deadlock – The Day the Arse Stood Still*. Ferdinand Mount (1992)

As a laxative Pantagruel 'swallows seventeen copper pills, each containing a man with pick and shovel, their goal being the location and dislodging of mounds of ordure; after they stack it in baskets and re-enter their pills'. Health is restored by vomiting out everything and everyone. Edmund D. Pellegrino (in Rhodes, 1980)

Desire

Pain wanders through my bones like a lost fire;
What burns me now? Desire, desire, desire.
Theodore Roethke (1986)

A man's genitals are naturally disobedient and self-willed, like a creature that will not listen to reason, and will do anything in their mad lust for possession. Much the same is true of the matrix or womb in women, which is a living creature within them which longs to bear children. And if it is left unfertilized long beyond the normal time, it causes extreme unrest, strays about the body, blocks the channels of the breath and causes in consequence acute distress and disorders of all kinds. This goes on until the woman's longing and the man's desire meet and pick the fruit from the tree, as it were, sowing the ploughland of the womb with seeds as yet unformed and too small to be seen, which take shape and grow within until they are born into the light of day as a complete living creature. Plato (1965)

Diabetes

One night I thirsted like a prince
Then like a king
Then like an empire   like a world
On fire . . .
. . . Months of having a tongue of flame convinced me: I had better
    not go
On this way . . .
When will the sugar rise boiling
Against me, and my brain be sweetened
To death?

James Dickey (1971)

Eating Disorders

There is the hunger for food, but there is also the great hunger, and that is to be part of creation. Sir Laurens van der Post

By the age of twenty-five, maybe a bit earlier, we are told she [St Catherine of Siena] ate 'nothing' . . . While dressing the cancerous breast sores of a woman she was tending, Catherine felt repulsed at the horrid odour of the suppuration. Determined to overcome all bodily sensations, she carefully gathered the pus into a ladle and drank it all. That night she envisioned Jesus inviting her to drink the blood flowing from his pierced side, and it was with this consolation that her stomach 'no longer had need of food and no longer could digest' . . . Notwithstanding the vast differences between Catherine's drive to be united with God and the modern day anorexic's quest for a sense of self, the psychological dilemma is similar. Rudolph M. Bell (1985)

Eye Problems

This sense of being in a place is less pronounced . . . Space is reduced to one's own body, and the position of the body is known not by what objects have been passed but by how long it has been in motion. Position is thus measured by time . . . For the blind, people are not there unless they speak . . . People are in motion, they are temporal, they come and they go. They come out of nothing, they disappear.

John Hull (1990)

Discovering an island
of blindness in one eye,
He saw at once what most
Can't see before they die –

The audacity of Spring
Shot through with light that came
Not from the sun, but from
some living inner flame;

A threat of blindness cured
his blindness; but how long
Could this new vision last? –
or was the whisper wrong

Which told him such an island
Without views must grow
To be a continent
Filling both eyes? – and so

He clasped the miracle
Of his discovered sight,
But saw approaching blindness
Like a black parasite . . .

Edward Lowbury (1968)

A blind man is different – his light is trapped
Outside a tabernacle gate.
His whole body must in light be draped
And all his face become an eye of fate.

Henry Shore (1976)

Fever

What's a fever but a fit of madness? William Shakespeare, *The Comedy of Errors*

So when a raging fever burns
We shift from side to side by turns,
And 'tis a poor relief we gain
To change the place but keep the pain.

Isaac Watts (1719)

By nightfall I was usually raving. My limbs went first, splintered like logs, so that I seemed to grow dozens of arms. Then the bed no longer had limits to it and became a desert of hot wet sand. I began to talk to a second head laid on the pillow, my own head once removed; it never talked back, but just lay there grinning very coldly into my eyes. The walls of the bedroom were the next to go; they began to bulge and ripple and roar, to flap like pastry, melt like sugar, and run bleeding with hideous hues. Then out of the walls, and down from the ceiling, advanced a row of intangible smiles; easy, relaxed, in no way threatening at first, but going on far too long. Even a maniac's smile will finally waver, but these just continued in silence, growing brighter, colder, and ever more humourless till the sick blood roared in my veins. They were Cheshire-cat smiles, with no face or outlines, and I could see the room clearly through them. But they hung above me like a stain on the air, a register of smiles in space, smiles without pity, smiles without love, smiling smiles of unsmiling smileness: not even smiles of strangers, but smiles of no one, expanding in brilliant silence, persistent, knowing, going on and on . . . till I was screaming and beating the bed rails.

At my scream all the walls shook down like a thunderclap and everything was normal again. The kitchen door opened, feet thumped on the stairs, and the girls bustled into the room. 'He's been seeing them faces again,' they whispered. 'It's all right!' they bawled. 'There, there! You won't see any more. Have a nice jug of lemon.' And they mopped me, and picked up the bedclothes. I lay back quietly while they fussed around; but what could I say to them? That I hadn't seen faces – that I'd only seen smiles? I tried that, but it got me nowhere.

Later, as the red night closed upon me, I was only barely conscious. I heard myself singing, groaning, talking, and the sounds were like hands on my body. Blood boiled, flesh crept, teeth clattered and clenched, my knees came up to my mouth; I lay in an evil swamp of sweat which alternately steamed and froze me. My shirt was a kind of enveloping sky wetly wrapping my goosy skin, and across which, at intervals, hot winds from Africa and Arctic blizzards blew. All objects in the room became molten again, and the pictures repainted themselves; things ran about, changed shape, grew monstrous, or trailed off into limitless distances. The flame of the candle threw shadows like cloaks which made everything vanish in turn, or it drew itself up like an ivory saint, or giggled and collapsed in a ball. I heard voices that couldn't control themselves, that either whispered just out of sound, or suddenly boomed some great echoing word, like 'Shovel!' or 'Old-men's-ears!' Such a shout would rouse me with terrible echoes, as though a piano had just been kicked by a horse.

It was myself, no doubt, who spoke these words, and the monologue went on for hours. Sometimes I deliberately answered back, but mostly I lay and listened, watching while the room's dark crevices began to smoke their ash-white nightmares . . . Such a night of fever slowed everything down as though hot rugs had been stuffed in a clock. I went gliding away under the surface of sleep, like a porpoise in tropic seas, heard the dry house echoing through caves of water, followed caverns through acres of dreams, then emerged through fathoms and years of experience, of complex lives and deaths, to find that the moon on the window had not moved an inch, that the world was not a minute older. Laurie Lee (1962)

Six weeks with fever is an eternity. Hours are like days. Honoré de Balzac (1977)

As a slave loves a beloved tyrant I love the vague tipsiness brought on by a slight fever, the flaccid, cold, penetrating discomfort in the very marrow of one's aching bones, one's burning eyes and pounding temples. It provides me with that tremulous, exhausted passivity in which I glimpse visions . . . Fernando Pessoa (1991)

From ancient times until the nineteenth century most diseases involved the quality of heat . . . which was understood as a cleansing and also an awakening of soul because fever is often accompanied by visions, strange dreams, hallucination. Fever is a heat that stimulates image. Robert Sardello (1992)

Fever is designed in part to magnify reality so that the imponderable contribution of the spirit to the 'malaise' which produces [the fever] can become visible. There seems to be deep within it a rounding up process of time which brings past, present and future lucidly together in the focus of a single symbol. Sir Laurens van der Post (1985)

Getting Up in the Morning

Some people say it is a very easy thing to get up of a cold morning. You have only, they tell you, to take the resolution, and the thing is done. This may be very true, just as a boy at school has only to take a flogging, and the thing is over. But we have not at all made up our minds upon it; and we find it a very pleasant exercise to discuss the matter, candidly, before we get up. Leigh Hunt (1846)

You sink down and muffle your head in the clothes, shivering all the while, but less from bodily chill, than the bare idea of a polar atmosphere. It is too cold even for the thoughts to venture abroad. You speculate on the luxury of wearing out a whole existence in bed, like an oyster in its shell, content with the sluggish ecstasy of inaction, and drowsily conscious of nothing but delicious warmth, such as you now feel again. Nathaniel Hawthorne (1839)

Guilt

In deep distress, I cried to God,
To God I cried, and told my grief;
He heard, and in my time of need
His goodness sent the wished relief.

But still I mourned, for though relieved,
I felt my heart of secret sin,
And though relieved from foes without,
I felt a lurking foe within.

Body and mind, by night and day,
Pressed on me with their baneful powers;
My frailties had disturbed my days,
And frightful dreams my midnight hours.

And when in sleep my eyelids close,
Short is the sweet repose of sleep;
I wake, but ah! I wake in vain –
Alas I only wake to weep.

My voice grows faint, my spirits droop,
And all of life within me dies;
I strive to utter my complaint,
But I can only breathe in sighs.

Oh for that grace to sinners given,
That grace so ample, rich and free!
Shall that which is vouchsafed to all
Be, oh my God, denied to me?

George Dyer

Illness of any sort was considered in Erewhon to be highly criminal
and immoral . . . I was liable, even for catching a cold, to be had up

before the magistrates and imprisoned for a considerable period. Samuel
Butler (1872)

> You do not have to be good.
> You do not have to walk on your knees
> for a hundred miles through the desert repenting.
> You only have to let the soft animal of your body
> love what it loves.
> Tell me about despair, yours, and I will tell you about mine.
> Meanwhile the world goes on.
> Meanwhile the sun and the clear pebbles of the rain
> are moving across the landscapes,
> over the prairies and the deep trees,
> the mountains and the rivers.
> Meanwhile the wild geese, high in the clean blue air,
> are heading home again.
> Whoever you are, no matter how lonely,
> the world offers itself to your imagination,
> calls to you like the wild geese, harsh and exciting –
> over and over announcing your place
> in the family of things.
> Mary Oliver (1986)

Headache

My head and the whole universe aches. Fernando Pessoa (1991)
  'I'm very brave generally,' he went on in a low voice, 'only today
I happen to have a headache!' Lewis Carroll (1871)

Heart Attack

Bad heart attack all day. Intermittency is very refined torture to one
who wants to live so very badly. Your pump goes 'dot and carry one',
or says 'misses a stitch', . . . you breathe deep, begin to shake your

friend's hand and make a farewell speech. Then it goes on again and you order another pint of beer.

It is a fractious animal within the cage of my thorax, and I never know when it is going to escape and make off with my precious life between its teeth. I humour and coax and soothe it, but, God wot, I haven't much confidence in the little beast. My thorax it appears is an intolerable kennel. W. N. P. Barbellion (1948)

While she was . . . holding on to the rail with a wet slippery hand, feeling the heat rise and thicken, the train belched again and this movement, much more powerful than before, shifted and heaved the people around her to enclose her in a kind of human tide. Her face now against a tweed back, she fought for breath . . .

. . . a huge pain took hold of her left arm, as if an iron claw had grasped it. She arched her back, tried to stretch her neck above assorted flesh and hair and smell. The train started, moved forward on a smooth glide, and as it did so the iron claws embraced her, like the appendages of a monster.

. . . There was no room in the train. Not one more passenger could have squeezed in. Yet as she sank to the floor and died they fell back, they shrank back and made the space for her she had needed for life. For dear life. Barbara Vine (1991)

Hypochondria

I remember going to the British Museum one day to read up the treatment for some slight ailment of which I had a touch – hay fever, I fancy it was. I got down the book, and read all I came to read; and then, in an unthinking moment, I idly turned the leaves, and began to indolently study diseases, generally. I forgot which was the first distemper I plunged into – some fearful, devastating scourge I know – and before I had glanced half down the list of 'premonitory symptoms', it was borne in upon me that I had fairly got it.

I sat for a while frozen with horror; and then in the listlessness of despair, I again turned over the pages. I came to typhoid fever – read the symptoms – discovered that I had typhoid fever, must have had it for months without knowing it – wondered what else I had got;

turned up St Vitus's dance – found, as I expected, that I had that too – began to get interested in my case, and determined to sift it to the bottom, and so started alphabetically – read up ague, and discovered that I was sickening for it, and that the acute stage would commence in about another fortnight. Bright's disease, I was relieved to find, I had only in a modified form, and, so far as that was concerned, I might live for years. Cholera I had with severe complications; and diphtheria I seemed to have been born with. I plodded conscientiously through the twenty-six letters, and the only malady I could conclude I had not got was housemaid's knee.

I felt rather hurt about this at first; it seemed somehow to be a sort of slight. Why hadn't I got housemaid's knee? Why this invidious reservation? After a while, however, less grasping feelings prevailed. I reflected that I had every other known malady in the pharmacology, and I grew less selfish, and determined to do without housemaid's knee. Gout, in its most malignant stage, it would appear, had seized me without my being aware of it; and zymosis I had evidently been suffering with from boyhood. There were no more diseases after zymosis, so I concluded there was nothing else the matter with me.
Jerome K. Jerome (1995)

George Eliot was sensitive, depressive and hypochondriacal, an absorber of medical textbooks and encyclopaedias. Richard Gordon (1993)

'Yes,' says the bandaged patient . . . to a group of friends much impressed, 'the doctor thinks there may be a slight anaesthesia of the prognosis, but he's sent my ear to New York and my appendix to Baltimore and a lock of my hair to the editors of all the medical journals, and meantime I am to keep very quiet and not exert myself beyond drinking a hot Scotch with lemon and nutmeg every half-hour.' With that he sinks back faintly on his cushions, luxuriously happy.
Stephen Leacock (1939)

> I wandered by the brookside,
> I wandered by the mill,
> I could not hear the brook flow,
> The noisy wheel was still;
> There was no burr of grasshopper

No chirp of any bird;
But the beating of my own heart
Was all the sound I heard.
Richard Monckton Milnes (1876)

We heard once of a man who went to bed with a cold one day and never got up again. The seizure was soon over and his health restored, but the adventure of being in bed impressed him deeply and he felt that he had discovered his niche at last. E. B. White (1990)

Indigestion (see also Bowel Problems)

Oft the teeming earth
Is with a kind of colic pinch'd and vex'd
By the imprisoning of unruly wind
Within her womb.
William Shakespeare, 1 Henry IV

Influenza

How the world has changed its shape; the tools of business grown remote; the sounds of festival become romantic like a merry-go-round heard across far fields; and friends have changed, some putting on a strange beauty, others deformed to the squatness of toads, while the whole landscape of life lies remote and fair, like the shore seen from a ship far out at sea, and [the invalid] is now exalted on a peak and needs no help from man or God, and now grovels on the floor glad of a kick from a housemaid . . . Virginia Woolf (1967)

Insomnia

When you're lying awake with a dismal headache, and repose is
    taboo'd by anxiety,
I conceive you may use any language you choose to indulge in,
    without impropriety;
For your brain is on fire – the bedclothes conspire of usual slumber
    to plunder you:
First your counterpane goes, and uncovers your toes, and your
    sheet slips demurely from under you;
Then the blanketing tickles – you feel like mixed pickles – so
    terribly sharp is the pricking,
And you're hot, and you're cross, and you tumble and toss till
    there's nothing 'twixt you and the ticking.
Then the bedclothes all creep to the ground in a heap, and you
    pick 'em all up in a tangle;
Next your pillow resigns and politely declines to remain at its
    usual angle!
Well, you get some repose in the form of a doze, with hot eyeballs
    and head ever aching,
But your slumbering teems with such horrible dreams that you'd
    very much better be waking . . .
W. S. Gilbert (1882)

That ridiculous repetitive voice that with its rehashed anxieties and
blurred recollections, keeps me company during insomnia. John Updike
(1989)

    Soon I ceased to sleep altogether, an acute attack of insomnia set
in, so terrible that it nearly made me go off my head. Insomnia does
not kill its man unless he kills himself – sleeplessness is the most
common cause of suicide. But it kills his *joie de vivre*, it saps his
strength, it sucks the blood from his brain and from his heart like a
vampire. It makes him remember during the night what he was meant
to forget in blissful sleep. It makes him forget during the day what he
was meant to remember. Axel Munthe (1949)

    Natural men have conceived a twofold use of sleep; that it is a refreshing of the body in this life; that it is a preparing of the soul for the next; that it is a feast, and it is the grace at that feast; that it is our recreation, and cheers us, and it is our catechism, and instructs us; we lie down in a hope that we will rise the stronger; and we lie down in a knowledge that we may rise no more. John Donne (1987)

Let him be safe in sleep
As leaves folded together
as young birds under wings
As the unopened flower.

Let him be hidden in sleep
As islands under rain,
as mountains with their clouds,
as hills in the mantle of dusk.

Let him be free in sleep
as the flowing tides of the sea,
as the travelling wind on the moor,
As the journeying stars in space.

Let him be upheld in sleep
In quiet waters of night
In the mirroring pool of dreams
Where memory returns in peace,
Where troubled spirit grows wise
And the heart is comforted.

Kathleen Raine (1988)

Come, Sleep, O Sleep, the certain knot of peace,
The baiting place of wit, the balm of woe,
The poor man's wealth, the prisoner's release,
The indifferent judge between the high and low;
With shield of proof shield me from out the press

Of those fierce darts Despair at me doth throw:
O make in me those civil wars to cease;
I will good tribute pay, if thou do so.

Sir Philip Sydney (1873)

Love and Hate

Come, doctor, use thy roughest art,
Thou canst not cruel prove;
Cut, burn, and torture every part,
To heal me of my love.

There is no danger, if the pain
Should me to a fever bring;
Compar'd with heats I now sustain,
A fever is so cool a thing.

Abraham Cowley (1647)

Oh ye gods, have ye ordained for every malady a medicine, for every sore a salve, for every pain a plaister, leaving only love remedyless.

John Lyly (1588)

I was angry with my friend:
I told my wrath, my wrath did end.
I was angry with my foe;
I told it not, my wrath did grow.

William Blake (1794)

Nausea

The solidity of things oppressed him. The rasp of a small stone underfoot made his stomach swoop. Grime on the wall round the stairwell light switch, and then the mass of the wall itself, the point-lessness of all those bricks, afflicted him, bore down on him like an illness. Was he hungry? The thought of taking selected parts of the solid world and passing them through a hole in his head and squeezing them through his guts was an abomination. He was pink and raw and dry. Ian McEwan (1990)

Obesity

Being fat is about knowing it. It is about a round-the-clock awareness that the fat person's body overflows the strict boundaries imposed on it by western social and cultural norms. To be a fat woman means to carry a double burden, for women are expected to conform to a more rigorous and stereotyped aesthetic ideal than are men. There is no way to hide being fat except by staying indoors. Shelley Bovey (1991)

You weigh your self worth on the bathroom scales. Martha Zinger

Obesity is a mental state, a disease brought on by boredom and disappointment. Cyril Connolly (1944)

Psoriasis

To be forgiven, by God: this notion so commonly mouthed in shadowy churches, was for me a tactile actuality as I lay in my loathed hide under that high hard pellet, that suspended white explosion, of a tropical sun. And the sun's weight on my skin always meant this to me; I was being redeemed, hauled back into mankind, back from deformity and shame. John Updike (1989)

To my body, which has no aesthetic criteria, psoriasis is normal, and its suppression abnormal. Psoriasis is my health. Its suppression constitutes a poisoning of the system, of my personal ecology . . . John Updike (1989)

Schizophrenia

'I took you right back to childhood – and earlier. I made you as the unborn in order to rest you.'

'That is the psychology of dementia praecox.'

'And it is sound psychology . . . If people would go back to Persephone when they needed to, they would not get dementia praecox. That is the thing you get when life is too hard for you.' Dion Fortune (1989)

The element's rage, the fiend voices that rave
Shall dwindle, shall blend,
Shall cease, shall become first a peace out of pain, then a light –
Robert Browning (1981)

Sexual Abuse

Incest victims are exhorted not to talk for fear of bringing shame on the family. And often the one who attempts to bring an abuse to light is shamed and blamed. Sandy Butler, in her book on incest, called *Conspiracy of Silence*, tells the story of Margaret, who attempted to get help when she discovered that her well-respected husband was abusing their children. Her husband's family told her she was overreacting, imagining things. Eventually she was hospitalized with a 'nervous breakdown'. School authorities and police ignored her pleas. Finally she turned to 'her personal source of solace and refuge' – the church. She discussed the problem at a meeting, asking for help. 'The people around her – people whom she had known, worked and worshipped with even before she was married – first expressed openness, then horror and disbelief, and finally masked their feelings behind expressionless faces. Margaret finished by asking for suggestions from anyone present as to what else she might try to do. She was answered by a muffled cough or two, the sound of bodies moving uncomfortably about on wooden chairs and nothing else. The next day Margaret was visited by two of the church's trustees. They told her that the church board had met that morning and had decided unanimously to recommend that she not attend any more church functions until she got this "straightened out at home".'

Another victim said, 'You come to believe that you're the crazy one and take all the responsibility for what is happening . . . You try lots of different ways to tell, and nobody is listening. So you stop trying and come to the only conclusion that is left to you. That it's you that is bad, and that if you hadn't been so bad Daddy wouldn't have had sex with you.'

We blame those who refuse to close their eyes for 'making a scene', while the victimizer is ignored, sympathized with, or forgotten. Starhawk (1987)

For people who have been abused and traumatized, silence is the greatest barrier to recovery. The breaking of secrecy is the beginning of healing. Through sharing stories the social bonds destroyed by incest are mended, and the traumatic experience is given new meaning in the retelling; it becomes a gift to others. Judith L. Herman (1978)

Shyness

Half the world seems to have confidence and half the world doesn't, and I don't know how to make the jump from one half to the other. In order to have confidence you have to be confident already: it's a vicious circle. Julian Barnes (1991)

I feel intimidated sometimes by having to say good morning to someone. My voice dries up, as if to pronounce the words out loud were an act of extraordinary audacity. It's a kind of embarrassment at my own existence . . . Fernando Pessoa (1991)

I was a total loner, not by self design. I just didn't know what the hell to say to people. I was so shy. I used to stammer and lisp and dribble at the mouth. Anthony Hopkins (1980)

Stuttering

He confirms an observation of mine, which indeed I find is hundreds of years old, that a stammering man is never a worthless one. Physiology can tell you why. It is an excess of delicacy, excess of sensibility to the presence of his fellow-creature, that makes him stammer. Thomas Carlyle (1888)

. . . I began to stutter with my own children. Their cheerful unblaming voices over the phone, and the apparition of their healthy round pale faces, summoned into my presence now by appointment and invitation, put a stopper in my throat. Stuttering had not been a problem for years. Suddenly I was afraid, again, of being misunderstood, of being mistaken for somebody else. I doubted my worthiness to mar the air with my voice. John Updike (1989)

Sunburn

When I hear modern people complain of being lonely then I know what has happened . . . What we lack is cosmic life, the sun in us and the moon in us. We can't get the sun in us by lying naked like pigs on a beach. The very sun that is bronzing us is inwardly disintegrating us – as we know later . . . We can only get the sun by a sort of worship, by going forth to worship the sun, worship that is felt in the blood. D. H. Lawrence (1995)

Toothache

For there was never yet philosopher
That could endure the toothache patiently.
William Shakespeare, *Much Ado about Nothing* v,i,35

My curse upon your venom'd stang,
That shoots my tortured gums alang;
And through my lugs[1] gies mony a twang,
    Wi' gnawing vengeance;
Tearing my nerves wi' bitter pang,
    Like racking engines!
Robert Burns (1993)

1. ears

Tuberculosis ('The Artist's Disease')

There is a dread disease which so prepares its victim, as it were, for death ... A dread disease in which the struggle between soul and body is so gradual, quiet and solemn, and the result so sure, that day by day, and grain by grain, the mortal part wastes and withers away, so that the spirit grows light and sanguine with its lightening load, and feeling immortality at hand, deems it but a new term in mortal life – a disease in which death and life are so strangely blended, that death takes a glow and hue of life, and life the gaunt and grisly form of death – a disease which medicine never cured, wealth warded off, or poverty could boast exemption from – which sometimes moves in giant strides, and sometimes at a tardy sluggish pace, but, slow or quick, it is ever sure and certain. Charles Dickens (1839)

It was all the fashion to suffer from chest complaint; everyone was consumptive, poets especially; it was good form to spit blood after each emotion that was at all inclined to be sensational, and to die before reaching thirty. Alexandre Dumas (1863)

19

Anxiety and Panic; Depression and Grief

Worry is a complete circle of inefficient thought whirling about a pivot of fear. Austen Fox Riggs

A merry heart doth good like a medicine; but a broken spirit drieth the bones. Proverbs xvii, 22

Anxiety, Panic and Other Disquiets of the Mind

The flesh endures the storms of the present alone, the mind those of the past and future as well. Epicurus

> Cans't though not minister to a mind diseas'd,
> Pluck from the memory a rooted sorrow,
> Raze out the written troubles of the brain;
> And with some sweet oblivious antidote
> Cleanse the stopped bosom of that perilous stuff
> Which weighs upon the heart?
> William Shakespeare, *Macbeth*, V, iii, 40–45

In the depths of every heart, there is a tomb and a dungeon, though the lights, music and revelry above may cause us to forget their existence, and the buried ones, or prisoners whom they hide. Nathaniel Hawthorne (1839)

Yesternight I pray'd aloud
In anguish and in agony,
Awakening from the fiendish crowd
Of shapes and thoughts that tortur'd me!
S. T. Coleridge (1802)

Panic, especially at night when the citadel darkens and the heroic ego sleeps, is a direct *participation mystique* in nature, a fundamental, even ontological experience of the world as alive and in dread. Objects become subjects, they move with life while one is oneself paralysed with fear. When existence is experienced through instinctual levels of fear, aggression, hunger or sexuality, images take on compelling life of their own . . . nature alive means Pan, and panic flings open a door into this reality. James Hillman (1998)

My whole life has been spent walking by the side of a bottomless chasm, jumping from stone to stone. Sometimes I try to leave my narrow path and join the swirling mainstream of life, but I always find myself drawn inexorably back towards the chasm's edge and there I shall walk until the day I finally fall into the abyss. For as long as I can remember I have suffered from a deep anxiety which I have tried to express in my art. Without anxiety and illness I would have been like a ship without a rudder. Edvard Munch

Ennui is the condition of not fulfilling our potentialities; remorse of not having fulfilled them; anxiety of not being able to fulfil them . . . Cyril Connolly (1944)

. . . when you don't have any money, the problem is food. When you have money, it's sex. When you have both, it's health you worry about . . . J. P. Donleavy (1956)

The neurotic is a criminal without the courage to commit a crime . . . Anxiety is repressed desire. Wilhelm Stekel (1923)

Perhaps worry is a device of nature to make us do our very best. John Chalmers Da Costa (1944)

Therefore do not be anxious about tomorrow, for tomorrow will be anxious for itself. Let the day's trouble be sufficient for the day. Matthew vi, 34

Depression

I have of late – but wherefore I know not – lost all my mirth, foregone all custom of exercises; and indeed it goes so heavily with my disposition that this goodly frame, the earth, seems to me a sterile promontory; this most excellent canopy the air, look you, this brave o'erhanging firmament, this majestical roof fretted with golden fire, why, it appears no other thing to me than a foul and pestilent con-gregation of vapours. What a piece of work is a man! How noble in reason! How infinite in faculty! In form and moving, how express and admirable! In action, how like an angel! In apprehension, how like a god! The beauty of the world! The paragon of animals! And yet, to me, what is this quintessence of dust? Man delights not me – no, nor woman neither. William Shakespeare, *Hamlet*, II, ii

William Cowper's mother died when he was five. He had a lifelong tendency to depression:

> What peaceful hours I once enjoy'd!
> How sweet their mem'ry still!
> But they have left an aching void,
> The world can never fill.
> William Cowper (1779)

> This glassy stream, that spreading pine,
> Those alders quivering to the breeze,
> Might soothe a soul less hurt than mine
> And please, if anything could please.

> But fix'd unalterable care
> Foregoes not what she feels within,
> Shows the same sadness ev'ry where,
> And slights the season and the scene.
> William Cowper (1791)

Man . . . drinks misery, and he tastes happiness; he mows misery and he gleans happiness; he journeys in misery, he does but walk in happiness; and what is worst, his misery is positive and dog-matical, his happiness is but disputable and problematical. John Donne (1987)

> The thoughts that rain their steady glow
> Like stars on life's cold sea,
> Which others know, or say they know –
> They never shone for me.
>
> Thoughts light, like gleams, my spirit's sky,
> But they will not remain.
> They light me once, they hurry by;
> And never come again.
>
> Matthew Arnold (1853)

Yet there are many who dare not kill themselves for fear of what the neighbours will say. Cyril Connolly (1944)

Grief

This poem featured in the film *Four Weddings and a Funeral*:

> Stop all the clocks, cut off the telephone,
> Prevent the dog from barking with a juicy bone,
> Silence the pianos and with muffled drum
> Bring out the coffin, let the mourners come.
>
> Let aeroplanes circle moaning overhead
> Scribbling on the sky the message He Is Dead,
> Put crêpe round the white necks of the public doves,
> Let the traffic policemen wear black cotton gloves.
>
> He was my North, my South, my East and West,
> My working week and my Sunday rest,
> My moon, my midnight, my talk, my song;
> I thought that love would last for ever: I was wrong.

The stars are not wanted now: put out every one;
Pack up the moon and dismantle the sun;
Pour away the ocean and sweep up the wood;
For nothing now can ever come to any good.
W. H. Auden (1967)

The film *Shadowlands* is about a great grief in the life of C. S. Lewis. Here he is writing on grief:

No one ever told me that grief felt so like fear. I am not afraid, but the sensation is like being afraid. The same fluttering in the stomach, the same restlessness, the yawning. I keep on swallowing.

At other times it feels like being mildly drunk, or concussed. There is a sort of invisible blanket between the world and me. I find it hard to take in what anyone says. Or perhaps, hard to want to take it in. It is so uninteresting. Yet I want the others to be about me. I dread the moments when the house is empty. If only they would talk to one another and not to me.

There are moments, most unexpectedly, when something inside me tries to assure me that I don't really mind so much, not so very much, after all. Love is not the whole of a man's life. I was happy before I ever met H. I've plenty of what are called 'resources'. People get over these things. Come, I shan't do so badly. One is ashamed to listen to this voice but it seems for a little to be making out a good case. Then comes a sudden jab of red-hot memory and all this common sense vanishes like an ant in the mouth of a furnace.

On the rebound one passes into tears and pathos. Maudlin tears. I almost prefer the moments of agony. These are at least clean and honest. But the bath of self-pity, the wallow, the loathsome sticky-sweet pleasure of indulging in it – that disgusts me . . .

I cannot talk to the children about her. The moment I try, there appears on their faces neither grief, nor love, nor fear, nor pity, but the most fatal of all non-conductors, embarrassment. They look as if I were committing an indecency. C. S. Lewis (1961)

One wept whose only child was dead,
New-born ten years ago.
'Weep not, he is in bliss,' they said.
She answered 'Even so,

'Ten years ago was born in pain
A child, not now forlorn.
But, oh, ten years ago, in vain,
A mother, a mother was born.'

Alice Meynell (1913)

Suppressed Grief

A grief without a pang, void, dark, and drear,
A stifled, drowsy, unimpassion'd grief,
Which finds no natural outlet, no relief
In word, or sigh, or tear.

S. T. Coleridge (1802)

All these white people that come here to make trouble for us are possessed by the troubled ghosts of their ancestors. This is because where the white men come from, people don't grieve. Because their dead are not at peace, the living cannot be either. This is terrible. These people are empty inside. Someone who does not have an inside cannot teach you anything. Malidoma Patrice Some (1995)

The Sorrow Passes

What I am saying here is, let the relative talk, cry, or scream if necessary. Let them share and ventilate, but be available. The relative has a long time of mourning ahead of him, when the problems for the dead are solved. He needs help and assistance from the confirmation of a so-called bad diagnosis until months after the death of a member of the family. Elizabeth Kubler-Ross (1979)

Let the tears which fell, and the broken words which were exchanged in the long close embrace between the orphans, be sacred. A father, sister, and mother, were gained, and lost in that one moment. Joy and grief were mingled in the cup; but they were no bitter tears: for even grief itself arose so softened, and clothed in such sweet and tender recollections, that it became a solemn pleasure, and lost all character of pain. Charles Dickens (1838)

Something quite unexpected has happened. It came this morning early. For various reasons, not in themselves at all mysterious, my heart was lighter than it had been for many weeks. For one thing, I suppose I am recovering physically . . . the sun was shining and there was a light breeze. And suddenly at the very moment when, so far, I mourned H. least, I remembered her best. Indeed, it was something (almost) better than memory; an instantaneous, unanswerable impression. To say it was like a meeting would go too far. Yet there was that in it which tempts me to use those words. It was as if the lifting of the sorrow removed a barrier. C. S. Lewis (1961)

Go into the shower-bath with a small quantity of water at a temperature low enough to give you a slight sensation of cold. Make no secret of low spirits to your friends but talk of them fully: they are always the worse for dignified concealment. Don't expect too much of human life, a sorry business at the best. Don't be too severe on yourself, or underrate yourself, but do yourself justice. Sidney Smith

You will forget your misery; you will remember it as waters that have passed away. Job xi, 16

The heart that breaks open can contain the whole universe. Joanna Macey (1983)

Out of the shell of the broken heart emerges the new-born soul. Hazrat Inayat Khan

> They may rail at this life – from the hour I began it,
> I've found it a life full of kindness and bliss;
> And until they can show me some happier planet,
> More social and bright, I'll content me with this.
> Thomas Moore (1801)

20

Madness

Minds like ruined cities, wrecked by madness. John Da Costa (1944)

Coming to Terms with Disturbed Minds

I am sitting across the table
eating my visit sandwich.
The one I bought him stays suspended
near his mouth; his eyes focus
on the table and seem to think,
his shoulders hunched forward.
I chew methodically,
pretending to take him
as a matter of course.
The sandwich tastes mad
and I keep chewing.
My past is sitting in front of me
filled with itself
and trying with almost no success
to bring the present to its mouth.

David Ignatow (1970)

A body seriously out of equilibrium, either with itself or with its environment, perishes outright. Not so a mind. Madness and suffering can set themselves no limit. George Santayana (1905)

Who are these? Why sit they here in twilight?
Wherefore rock they, purgatorial shadows,
Drooping tongues from jaws that slob their relish,
Baring teeth that leer like skulls' teeth wicked?
Stroke on stroke of pain, – but what slow panic,
Gouged these chasms round their fretted sockets?
Ever from their hair and through their hands' palms
Misery swelters. Surely we have perished
Sleeping, and walk hell; but who these hellish?
– These are men whose minds the dead have ravished.

Wilfred Owen (1963)

Madness from the Inside: A Diseased Form of Wisdom

Today . . . I experienced a singular premonition, I felt pass over me
a breath of wind from the wings of madness. Charles Baudelaire

> Hatred and vengeance, my eternal portion,
> Scarce can endure delay of execution,
> Wait, with impatient readiness, to seize my
> Soul in a moment . . .
>
> William Cowper (1997)

O the mind, mind has mountains; cliffs that fall
frightful, sheer, no-man-fathomed. Hold them cheap
may who ne'er hung there. Nor does long our small
Durance deal with that steep or deep. Here! creep,
Wretch, under a comfort serves in a whirlwind: all
Life death does end and each day dies with sleep.

Gerard Manley Hopkins (1967)

'You're ill from overworking, you've worn yourself out. I'm trying
to say that you've sacrificed your health for an idea and it won't be
long before you've sacrificed your life to it. What could be better? All
noble spirits blessed with gifts from on high have this as their aim.'

'If I *know* that I'm mentally ill, how can I have any faith in myself?'

'But how do you know that men of genius, in whom the whole world puts its faith, haven't seen ghosts too? Nowadays scientists say genius is akin to madness. My friend, only the mediocre, the common herd, are healthy and normal. Thoughts about an age of neurosis, overwork, degeneracy and so on can seriously worry only those for whom the purpose of life lies in the present – that is, the common herd.'

'The Romans used to speak of *mens sana in corpore sano*.'

'Not all that the Greeks and Romans said is true. Heightened awareness, excitement, ecstasy – everything that distinguishes prophets, poets, martyrs to an idea, from ordinary people is hostile to man's animal side – I mean his physical health. I repeat: if you want to be healthy and normal, go and join the herd.' Anton Chekhov (1984)

On the floor near his face, he saw a large pool of blood and was too weak now to say one word, but an ineffable boundless happiness flooded his whole being . . . the black monk whispered to him that he was a genius and that he was dying only because his weak human body had lost its balance and could no longer serve to house a genius. Anton Chekhov (1984)

The Meaning in Madness

What's madness but nobility of soul
At odds with circumstance?
Theodore Roethke (1986)

A little madness in the spring
Is wholesome even for the King.
Emily Dickinson (1983)

Much Madness is divinest Sense –
To a discerning Eye –
Much Sense – the starkest madness –
Emily Dickinson (1983)

Lovers and madmen have such seething brains,
Such shaping fantasies that apprehend
More than cool reason ever comprehends.

William Shakespeare, *A Midsummer Night's Dream*, V, i, 4–6

Through my work with the patients I realized that paranoid ideas and hallucinations contain a germ of meaning. A personality, a life history, a pattern of hopes and desires lie behind the psychosis. The fault is ours if we do not understand them . . . At bottom we discover nothing new and unknown in the mentally ill; rather, we encounter the substratum of our own natures. C. G. Jung (1987)

For thee the fates, severely kind, ordain
A cool suspense from pleasure and from pain,
Thy life a long, dead calm of fix'd repose;
No pulse that riots, and no blood that glows.
Still as the sea, 'ere winds were taught to blow,
Or moving spirit bade the waters flow.

Alexander Pope (1751)

'How fortunate Buddha, Muhammad or Shakespeare were not being treated by kind-hearted relatives for ecstasy and inspiration!' Kovrin said. 'If Muhammad had taken potassium bromide for his nerves, had worked only two hours a day and drunk milk, then that remarkable man would have left as much to posterity as his dog. In the long run doctors and kind relatives will turn humanity into a lot of morons. Mediocrity will pass for genius and civilization will perish . . .' Anton Chekhov (1984)

Sanity is madness put to good uses; waking life is a dream controlled. George Santayana (1905)

The island is a bit cramped and . . . life on it is pretty meagre and plagued with all sorts of imaginary wants because too much life has been left outside, and . . . as a result a terrifying monster is created, or rather roused out of its slumbers . . . this seemingly alarming animal stands in a secret compensatory relationship to the island and could supply everything that the island lacks. C. G. Jung (1966a)

21

Pain

The useless, unjust, incomprehensible, inept abomination that is physical pain. Joris-Karl Huysmans (1959)
   Pain is one malady with many names. Antiphanes

Trying to Describe Pain

The 'pain' of which a history needs to be written is the . . . intrinsic, personalized experience designated by the expression 'my pain' . . . I have no doubt about the reality of pain-experience, but I cannot really tell anybody what I experience. Ivan Illich (1975)
   Some of the following words describe your present pain. Circle the one word in each group that best describes it. Mark only one word in each group. Skip the group that does not apply.

1	2	3	4
Flickering	Jumping	Pricking	Sharp
Quivering	Flashing	Boring	Cutting
Pulsing	Shooting	Drilling	Lacerating
Throbbing			Stabbing
Beating			Lancinating

5	6	7	8
Pinching	Tugging	Hot	Tingling
Pressing	Pulling	Burning	Itchy
Gnawing	Wrenching	Scalding	Smarting
Cramping		Searing	Stinging
Crushing			

9	10	11	12
Dull	Tender	Tiring	Sickening
Sore	Taut	Exhausting	Suffocating
Hurting	Rasping		
Aching	Splitting		
Heavy			

13	14	15	16
Fearful	Punishing	Wretched	Annoying
Frightful	Gruelling	Blinding	Troublesome
Terrifying	Cruel	Miserable	
	Vicious	Intense	
	Killing	Unbearable	

17	18	19	20
Spreading	Tight	Cool	Nagging
Radiating	Numb	Cold	Nauseating
Penetrating	Drawing	Freezing	Agonizing
Piercing	Squeezing		Dreadful
Tearing	Torturing		

Patient Pain Assessment Questionnaire, University of Iowa Hospitals and Clinics

He stirred, shifting his body; then the pain
Leapt like a prowling beast, and gripped and tore
His groping dreams with grinding claws and fangs.
Siegfried Sassoon (1961)

The Experience of Pain

. . . I am bound
Upon a wheel of fire that mine own tears
Do scald like molten lead.
William Shakespeare, *King Lear* IV, vii, 46–8

Whether or not pain is the most difficult part of cancer to live through, it is probably the hardest to describe. We have plenty of words to describe the specific pains: sharp, throbbing, piercing, burning, even dull. But these words do not describe the experience of pain. We lack terms to express what it means to live 'in' such pain. Unable to express pain, we come to believe there is nothing to say. Silenced, we become isolated in pain, and the isolation increases the pain. Like the sick feeling that comes with the recognition of yourself as ill, there is a pain attached to being in pain. Arthur Frank (1991)

A man with the toothache thinks everyone happy whose teeth are sound. George Bernard Shaw

> My curse upon your venom'd stang,
> That shoots my tortured gums alang;
> And through my lugs[1] gies mony a twang,
>   Wi' gnawing vengeance;
> tearing my nerves wi' bitter pang,
>   Like racking engines!
>
> When fevers burn, or ague freezes,
> Rheumatics gnaw, or colic squeezes;
> Our neighbour's sympathy may ease us,
>   Wi' pitying moan;
> but thee – thou hell o' a' diseases,
>   Aye mocks our groan!
>
> Adown my beard the slavers trickle!
> I kick the wee stools o'er the mickel,
> As round the fire the giglets keckle,[2]
>   To see me loup;[3]
> While, raving mad, I wish a heckle[4]
>   Were in their doup.[5]
>
> Robert Burns (1993)

> Once could the morn's first beams, the healthful breeze,
> All nature charm, and gay was every hour; –
> But ah! not Music's self, nor fragrant bower
> Can glad the trembling sense of wan Disease.

1. ears 2. girls giggle 3. leap 4. flax comb 5. buttocks

Now that the frequent pangs my frame assail,
Now that my sleepless eyes are sunk and dim,
And seas of pain seem waving through each limb –
Ah what can all life's gilded scenes avail?
I view the crowds whom Youth and Health inspire,
Hear the loud laugh and catch the sportive lay,
Then sigh and think – I too could laugh and play
And gaily sported on the Muse's lyre,
Ere Tyrant Pain had chas'd away delight,
Ere the wild pulse throbb'd anguish thro' the night!
S. T. Coleridge (1969)

I wish it were the fashion to groan when one is ill. I like groaning, and I believe it helps me to bear the suffering . . . But modern sickroom practice is all against groaning. In Victorian times it was different . . . Their roars were an inspiration to their doctors and nurses, urging them on to greater flights of bleeding, purging, leeching and poulticing. Furthermore groaning has curative powers. A Hindu, when he is ill, repeats the mystic syllable 'Om' as loudly and resonantly as he can until he is well . . . Robertson Davies (1986)

Pain has an element of Blank –
It cannot recollect
When it began – or if there were
A day when it was not –.

It has no future – but itself –
Its infinite realms contain
Its Past – enlightened to perceive
New Periods – of Pain.
Emily Dickinson (1983)

Making a Working Relationship with Pain

I have given a name to my pain and call it 'dog'. It is just as faithful, just as obtrusive and shameless, just as entertaining, just as clever as any other dog – and I can scold it and vent my bad mood on it, as others do with their dogs, servants, and wives. Friedrich Nietzsche (1974)

Pain as Protector

Pain is capable of exciting the organs into activity: it is the guardian of human life. Sir Charles Bell (1824)

At certain moments my body is illuminated . . . suddenly I see into myself . . . I can make out the depth of the layers of my flesh; and I feel zones of pain, rings, poles, plumes of pain. Paul Valéry (1973)

A new-born child does not realize that his body is more a part of himself than surrounding objects . . . and it is only by degrees, through pain, that he understands the fact of the body. W. Somerset Maugham (1990)

22

Disability

. . . all those who cannot walk – and instead try to fly. Robert Murphy (1987)

The Disobedient Body

Sit on the bed. I'm blind, and three parts shell.
Be careful; can't shake hands now; never shall.
Both arms have mutinied against me, – brutes.
My fingers fidget like ten idle brats.

I tried to peg out soldierly, – no use!
One dies of war like any old disease.
Wilfred Owen (1963)

The darkness and silence of the tomb were around her. No mother's smile called forth her answering smile, no father's voice taught her to imitate sounds – they, brothers and sisters, were but forms of matter which resisted her touch, but which differed not from the furniture of the house, save in warmth, and in the power of locomotion; and not even in these respects from the dog and the cat.

But the immortal spirit which had been implanted within her could not die, nor be maimed or mutilated; and though most of its avenues of communication with the world were cut off, it began to manifest itself through the others. As soon as she could walk she began to explore the room . . . Charles Dickens (1860); on a visit to a home for the blind in Boston, when he met an eight-year-old blind, deaf and dumb girl with almost no sense of smell or taste

'They've made a new woman of me,' she said, 'so I can go home now.' She can't go home. She feels like a new woman because she is properly medicated, made to eat three meals a day and has distractions. She has ditched the memories of her recent, dismal life and thinks she'll go back to the days when she was active and had friends, not twenty-three hours a day on her own, drugged, sobbing, not eating. 'Have I got to stay here for the rest of my life?' she cried on the phone. 'You bitch,' she screamed. I hung up.

Everyone told us to stay away, that each time she saw us she would be reminded of the past and of what she had lost, that the sight of us would make her agitated as she pleaded to be taken home; the past had to be allowed to wither in her memory. So we stayed away. The second time I went to see her it almost broke my heart. She *had* settled in, and in doing so had become institutionalized. With the face of an orphan, she now meekly does as she is told, sits where she is told to, eats food I know she does not like. Linda Grant (1996)

> Less even than animals can they imagine
> meaning. Words waft past them uselessly,
> but the music becomes their being:
>
> It beats to their pulses: they are careful of its feel;
> It is beauty, in its colour, order, wholeness.
> It is almost language. They nearly respond.
> Ann Ward (1974); on a therapy class for brain-damaged children

Attitudes to Disability

All of them touch him like some queer disease. Wilfred Owen (1963)

My life is not really very different from how non-disabled people feel about themselves. It is simply that they wear a cloak of normality, a concept which renders me naked . . . We both live in the shadow of a stereotype. I'm simply lucky enough to be on the fringe, rejected by the stereotype, forced to forge my own identity, my own reality, and to create it anew . . . beautiful, proud and disabled. Mary Duffy (1982)

Why this distancing of the chronically ill and handicapped? Why are we so threatening that we must be made socially invisible? Anything that separates and negates those with a chronic condition will ultimately invalidate not only them but everyone else. Mary Duffy (1982)

The Disabled Person's Struggle

The impact of losing his legs never hit Bader in one moment, or even in a day or a week. The realization formed slowly in a doped mind, which was merciful. Against the agonizing urgency of the pain it was only a detail, and when the pain ebbed and allowed other things to matter his feelings were cushioned by dope that left him floating easily and somewhat detached in a tranquil unreal present, unmindful of any future. Joyce came in later that day and said, 'Sorry, old man, but I had to take the other leg off below the knee. I couldn't save it. You're really lucky to be in the world still.'

'That's all right, sir,' Bader said, 'I'll get some longer legs. I always wanted to be taller.' Paul Brickhill (1957)

One day he cried and cried and cried because he had messed his sheets and so was no better than the incontinents. No one knew, of course, that those clean grey flannel shorts he had entered the hospital with . . . had been bought for him to mark the day he had learned to indicate with a movement of his left hand and jerk of his eyes that he wished to be taken to the toilet. A moment of special growing up . . . Yet so weak was he by then that he could not even cry out his misery at having messed his legs and sheets. William Horwood (1988)

Although I couldn't talk very much at seven years old, I was now able to sit up alone and crawl about from place to place on my bottom without breaking any bones or smashing any of my mother's china. I wore no shoes or any other kind of footwear. My mother had tried to make me used to having my feet covered from an early age, saying I looked very much neglected barefooted. But whenever she put anything on my feet I always kicked it off again quickly. I hated having my feet covered. When mother put shoes or stockings on my feet, I felt as any normal person might feel if his hands were tied behind his back.

As time went on, I began to depend more and more on my left foot for everything. It was my means of communication, of making myself understood by the family. Very slowly it became indispensable to me. With it I learned to break down some of the barriers that stood between me and the others at home. It was the only key to the door of the prison I was in. Christy Brown (1972)

He had nothing left to hold on to, nothing but a body he did not want. He was a boy far along the road to death, the only road along which he was able to walk as if he were normal: along which he could now run . . .

It was then, in those final fading moments that, for the first time since Arthur had been put away, he heard the Skallagrigg call his name . . .

So did the Skallagrigg come to Arthur that first time as he lay dying in his bed, with those eyes of a dead patient staring at him from across the ward and the light growing stronger. Our Arthur turned a little, a great effort for him, and whispered that name he loved and which loved him; and he knew that he must live. William Horwood (1988)

23

Growing Old

Like a flower we have our store
Of the world's short-lived vigour.
Goronwy Owen (1876)

Old age is a hospital that takes in all diseases. German proverb

The End of Youth

There is no doubt when old age begins. The human body is a furnace which keeps in blast three score years and ten, more or less. It burns about three hundred pounds of carbon a year (besides other fuel) when in fair working order, according to a great chemist's estimate. When the fire slackens, life declines; when it goes out, we are dead.

  It has been shown by some noted French experimenters, that the amount of combustion increases up to about the thirtieth year, remains stationary unto about forty-five, and then diminishes. This last is the point where old age starts from. The great fact of physical life is the perpetual commerce with the elements, and the fire is the measure of it. Oliver Wendell Holmes (1858)

> But now at thirty years my hair is grey –
> (I wonder what it will be like at forty?
> I thought of a peruke the other day –)
> My heart is not much greener; and, in short, I
> Have squandered my whole summer while 'twas May,
> And feel no more the spirit to retort; I

Have spent my life, both interest and principal,
And deem not, what I deemed, my soul invincible.
Lord Byron (1819–24)

Maturity

Though you are young and I am old,
Though your veins hot, and my blood cold,
Though youth is moist and age is dry;
Yet embers live when flames do die.

The tender graft is easily broke,
But who will shake the sturdy oak?
You are more fresh and fair than I;
Yet stubs do live when flowers do die.

Thou, that thy youth doth vainly boast,
Know buds are soonest nipped with frost:
Think that thy fortune still dost cry,
'Thou fool! tomorrow thou must die.'
Thomas Campion (1909)

Dr Oliver Wendell Holmes once laid out the dictum that the key to longevity was to have a chronic incurable disease and take good care of it. Lewis Thomas (1983)

Decline

Ageing: the ever-shrinking perimeter of pleasure. Igor Stravinsky

Old age, a second child, by nature curs'd
With more and greater evils than the first,
Weak, sickly, full of pains; in every breath
Railing at life, and yet afraid of death.
Charles Churchill (1764)

> Last scene of all,
> That ends this strange eventful history,
> Is second childishness and mere oblivion,
> Sans teeth, sans eyes, sans taste, sans everything.
>
> William Shakespeare, *As You Like It* II, vii, 163–6

We often see a man pass away by degrees, and limb by limb lose the sensation of life: first the toes of the feet grow livid, and the nails, next die feet and legs, and afterwards over the other limbs go creeping the cold footsteps of death. Lucretius (1805)

> The weariness, the fever and the fret
> Here where men sit and hear each other groan;
> Where palsy shakes a few, sad, last gray hairs,
> Where youth grows pale, and spectre-thin and dies.
>
> John Keats (1969)

Today you lose a tooth, tomorrow a hair, a sore opens, an abscess forms, blisters are raised on you, drains are inserted. Add to all these corns on your feet, bad natural smells of every kind and flavour, and you have a most inspiring picture of the human person. To think that one loves all this! that one loves oneself, and that I, for one, have the nerve to look at myself in the mirror without bursting into laughter. Isn't the mere sight of an old pair of boots profoundly sad and melancholy! when you think of all the steps you have taken in them . . . the cracked leather seems to tell you: 'and now, you fool, go and buy another pair . . .' Gustave Flaubert

> But Stella, say, what evil tongue
> Reports you are no longer young;
> That time sits with his scythe to mow
> Where erst sat Cupid with his bow;
> That half your locks are turned to grey?
> I'll ne'er believe a word they say.
> 'Tis true, but let it not be known,
> My eyes are somewhat dimmish grown;
> For nature always in the right,

To your decays adapts my sight,
And wrinkles undistinguished pass,
For I'm ashamed to use a glass;
And till I see them with these eyes,
Whoever says you have them, lies.

Jonathan Swift (1983)

24

Facing Death

First our pleasures die – and then
Our hopes, and then our fears – and when
These are dead, the debt is due,
Dust claims dust – and we die, too.
P. B. Shelley

No man is an island, entire of itself; every man is a piece of the continent, a part of the main; if a clod be washed away by the sea, Europe is the less, as well as if a promontory were; any man's death diminishes me, because I am involved in mankind; and therefore never send to know for whom the bell tolls; it tolls for thee. John Donne (1987)

Awareness of Mortality

I inhabit a weak, frail, decayed tenement; battered by the winds and broken in on by storms, and, from all I can learn, the landlord does not intend to repair. John Quincy Adams

Then one night, while sweating through another attack, which seemed no different from any of the others, I was given a shock which affected me with an almost voluptuous awe. As usual my fever had flared up sharply, and I was tossing in its accustomed fires, when I woke up, clear-headed, somewhere in the middle of the night, to find the whole family round my bed. Seven pairs of eyes stared in dread surmise, not at me but at something in me. Mother stood helplessly wringing her hands, and the girls were silently weeping. Even Harold, who could usually shrug off emotion, looked pale and strained in the candlelight.

I was surprised by their silence and the look in their eyes, a mixture of fear and mourning. What had suddenly brought them in the dark of the night to stand blubbing like this around me? I felt warm and comfortable, completely relaxed, and amused as though somehow I'd fooled them. Then they all started whispering, around me, about me, across me, but never directly to me.

'He's never been like this before,' said one. 'Hark at his awful rattle.'

'He's never had that ghastly colour either.'

'It's cruel – the poor little mite.'

'Such a gay little chap, he was, boo-hoo.'

'There, there, Phyl; don't you fret.'

'D'you think the vicar would come at this hour?'

'Someone had better run and fetch him.'

'We'd better knock up Jack Halliday, too. He could bike down and fetch the doctor.'

'We'll have to sit up, Ma. His breathing's horrible.'

'Perhaps we should wire his dad . . .'

Perfectly conscious, I heard all of this, and was tempted to join in myself. But their strangeness of tone compelled my silence, some peculiar threat in their manner, and a kind of fearful reverence in their eyes and voices as though they saw in me shades of the tomb. It was then that I knew that I was very ill; not by pain, for my body felt normal. Silently the girls began to prepare for their vigil, wrapping their shawls around them. 'You go get some rest, Ma – we'll call you later.' They disposed themselves solemnly round the bed, folded their hands in their laps, and sat watching my face with their hollow eyes for the first signs of fatal change. Held by the silence of those waiting figures, in that icy mid-hour of the night, it came to me then, for the first time in my life, that it was possible I might die.

I remember no more of that sombre occasion, I think I just fell asleep – my eyelids closing on a shroud of sisters which might well have been my last sight on earth. When I woke next morning to their surprise, the crisis was apparently over. And save for that midnight visitation, and for the subsequent behaviour of the village, I would never have known my danger.

I remained in Mother's bedroom for many weeks, and a wood-fire burned all day. School friends, as though on a pilgrimage, came in their best clothes to bring me flowers. Girls sent me hens' eggs pencilled with kisses; boys brought me their broken toys. Even my schoolteacher (whose heart was of stone) brought me a bagful of sweets and nuts. Finally Jack, unable to keep the secret any longer, told me I'd been prayed for in church, just before collections, twice, on successive Sundays. My cup was full, I felt immortal; very few had survived that honour. Laurie Lee (1962)

Fighting Death or Facing Death

Teach him to live rather than to avoid death; life is not breath, but action, the use of our senses, our mind, our faculties, every part of ourselves which makes us conscious of our being. J.-J. Rousseau

O day! he cannot die
When thou so fair art shining!
O Sun, in such a glorious sky,
So tranquilly reclining;

He cannot leave thee now,
While fresh west winds are blowing,
And all around his youthful brow
Thy cheerful light is glowing!

Beside thee, on my knee,
My fairest friend, I pray
That thou to cross the eternal sea
Wouldst yet one hour delay:

. . . One look that sore reproved me
For the woe I could not bear –
One mute look of suffering moved me
To repent my useless prayer . . .

Emily Brontë (1846)

Berta. Berta . . .

my father calls.
My mother waits outside his door.
Doctors, nurses work machines
to pump his lungs with air,
shock his heart to rhythmic pulse.

Wired with electronic plugs, he twitches
still calls for his wife.

Banned from his bedside,
my mother is told
she would be in the way.

Against my father's flesh,
cold metal of defibrillator.
  His life
  one dot
   spiralling the monitor.
Through the whirring humming clicking

  Berta . . .

Silence.

The machines are rolled from his room
to the next ward.

My mother is told.

  'Can I see him now?'
No. Says Nurse. We have a special waiting-room.

My father grows cold.

His lips
still open
with my mother's name.
Helen Blitzer

He may cry out for rest, peace, dignity, but he will get infusions, transfusions, a heart machine, or a tracheostomy. He may want one single person to stop for one single minute so that he can ask one single question – but he will get a dozen people around the clock, all busily preoccupied with his heart rate, pulse, electrocardiogram or pulmonary functions, his secretions or excretions, but not with him as a human being. He may wish to fight it all but it is going to be a useless fight since all this is done in the fight for his life, and if they can save his life they can consider the person afterwards. Those who consider the person first may lose precious time to save his life! At least this seems to be the rationale or justification behind all this – or is it? Is the reason for this increasingly mechanical, depersonalized approach our own defensiveness? Is this approach our own way to cope with and repress the anxieties that a terminally or critically ill patient evokes in us? Elizabeth Kubler-Ross (1979)

Whether it was morning or evening, Friday or Sunday, made no difference, it was all one and the same: gnawing, agonizing pain never ceasing for an instant, the consciousness of life inexorably ebbing away but not yet gone; the relentless approach of that ever dreaded and hateful death which was the only reality, and all this lying going on at the same time. What were days, or weeks, or hours of the day to him?

'Wouldn't you like some tea, sir?' Leo Tolstoy (1960)

Whether to Tell the Patient the Truth

I asked the wife whether her husband was aware of the diagnosis and if he realized he was extremely ill. She said that she was not sure because they never talked about his ill health.

Being a good conscientious doctor I felt that the truth should be brought into the open and went back into the bedroom.

'Do you know what is wrong with you?' I asked.

'Yes, I have cancer,' he replied.

'Do you know how ill you are?' I continued.

'Yes, I know I am dying.'

'Have you talked to your wife about this?' I asked.

'No, I do not want to worry her,' he replied.

As I left the house his wife said with a sigh: 'So he knows, and there is no use in pretending any more.'

Seeing her face I realized I had betrayed her trust in me and acted against the wishes of the couple in my misplaced desire to help.

The next day the patient's condition deteriorated and he went into hospital.

. . . My wish to bring everything out into the open had destroyed the delicate fabric of denial which had been built up between these two people as a coping mechanism. As with many experiences within my working life, I felt humbled, but grateful to learn such an important lesson from my patients. Dr Christine R. Page (1992)

I believe the question should not be stated, 'Do I tell my patient?' but should be rephrased as, 'How do I share this knowledge with my patient?' The physician should first examine his own attitude towards malignancy and death so that he is able to talk about such grave matters without undue anxiety. He should listen for cues from the patient which enable him to elicit the patient's willingness to face the reality. The more people in the patient's environment who know the diagnosis of malignancy, the sooner the patient himself will realize the true state of affairs anyway, since few people are actors enough to maintain a believable mask over a long period of time. Most if not all of the patients know anyway. They sense it by the changed attention, by the new and different approach that people take to them, by the lowering of voices or the avoidance of rounds, by a tearful face of a relative or an ominous, smiling member of the family who cannot hide their true feelings. They will pretend not to know when the doctor or relative is unable to talk about their true condition, and they will welcome someone who is willing to talk about it but allows them to keep their defences as long as they have need of them. Elizabeth Kubler-Ross (1979)

What tormented Ivan Ilyich most was the pretence, the lie, which for some reason they all kept up, that he was merely ill and not dying, and that he need only stay quiet and carry out the doctor's orders, and then some great change for the better would result. But *he* knew that whatever they might do nothing would come of it except still more agonizing suffering and death . . . And it was a strange thing – many a time when they were playing their farce for his benefit he was within a hair's breadth of shouting at them: 'Stop lying! You know, and I know, that I am dying. So do at least stop lying about it!' But he had never had the spirit to do it. The awful, terrible act of his dying was, he saw, reduced by those about him to the level of a fortuitous, disagreeable and rather indecent incident (much in the same way as people behave with someone who goes into a drawing-room smelling unpleasantly) – and this was being done in the name of the very decorum he had served all his life long. He saw that no one felt for him, because no one was willing even to appreciate his situation.

Leo Tolstoy (1960)

Ready to Die

Death is the poor man's best physician. Irish proverb

> Mild was the slow necessity of death;
> The tranquil spirit failed beneath its grasp,
> Without a groan, almost without a fear,
> Calm as a voyager to some distant land,
> And full of wonder, full of hope as he.
>
> P. B. Shelley (1813)

> Spare me the whispering, crowded room,
> The friends who come and gape, and go;
> The ceremonious air of gloom –
> All that makes death a hideous show!

> Nor bring, to see me cease to live,
> Some doctor full of phrase and fame,
> To shake his sapient head and give
> The ill he cannot cure a name.

Bring none of these; but let me be,
While all around in silence lies,
Moved to the window near, and see
Once more, before my dying eyes,

Bathed in the sacred dews of morn
The wide aërial landscape spread –
The world which was ere I was born,
The world which lasts when I am dead;

There let me gaze, till I become
In soul, with what I gaze on, wed!
To feel the universe my home;
To have before my mind – instead

Of the sick room, the mortal strife,
The turmoil for a little breath –
The pure eternal course of life,
Not human combatings with death!

Thus feeling, gazing might I grow
Composed, refreshed, ennobled, clear;
Then willing let my spirit go
To work or wait elsewhere or here.

Matthew Arnold (1867)

Longing for Death

Death is the liberator of him whom freedom cannot release; the physician of him whom medicine cannot cure; the comforter of him whom time cannot console. Walter Colton

Living is an illness to which sleep provides the relief every sixteen hours. The cure is death. Sebastian Chamfort

I ask but that my death may find
The freedom to my life denied;
Ask but the folly of mankind,
Then, at last, to quit my side.
Matthew Arnold (1853)

Euthanasia

O Death the healer, scorn thou not I pray,
To come to me; of cureless ills
Thou art the one physician.
Aeschylus (1976)

I have been half in love with easeful death . . .
Now more than ever seems it rich to die,
To cease upon the midnight with no pain.
John Keats (1969)

Spirit of death, so still, so slow,
Must I too go
To twilight years, the tedious downward path?
Must I too live this fading aftermath
And feel my heart grow cold?
Oh come be swift and take me while I stand,
My work still strong beneath a steady hand,
A life that ne'er grew old.
John Bruce MacCallum (1938)

Pale death, the grand physician, cures all pain,
The dead rest well who lived for joys in vain.
John Clare (1970)

'To hasten night would be humane,'
I, a doctor, beg a doctor,
for still the darkness will not come –
his sunset slow, his first star pain.

> I plead: 'We know another law.
> For one maimed bird we'd do as much,
> and if a creature need not suffer
> must he, for etiquette, endure?'
>
> Dannie Abse (1989)

'Please,' he begs me. In his open mouth, upon his teeth, a brown paste of saliva. All night long he has thrashed, as though to hollow out a grave in the bed.

'I won't let you suffer,' I tell him. In his struggle the sheet is thrust aside. I see the old abandoned incision, the belly stuffed with tumour. His penis even is skinny. One foot with five blue toes is exposed. In my cupped hand, they are cold. I think of the twenty bones of that foot laced together with tendon, each ray accompanied by its own nerve and artery. Now, this foot seems a beautiful dead animal that had once been trained to transmit the command of a man's brain to the earth.

'I'll get rid of the pain,' I tell his wife.

But there is no way to kill the pain without killing the man who owns it. Morphine to the lethal dose . . . and still he miaows and bays and makes other sounds like a boat breaking up in a heavy sea. I think his pain will live on long after he dies.

'Please,' begs his wife, 'we cannot go on like this.'

'Do it,' says the old woman, his mother. 'Do it now.'

'To give him any more would kill him,' I tell her.

'Then do it,' she says. Richard Selzer (1980)

> Thou shalt not kill; but need not strive
> Officiously to keep alive.
>
> Arthur Hugh Clough (1849)

Suicide

> One more unfortunate
> Weary of breath
> Rashly importunate
> Gone to her death!

Take her up tenderly,
Lift her with care:
Fashioned so slenderly,
Young, and so fair!

Touch her not scornfully;
Think of her mournfully,
Gently and humanly:
Not of the stains of her –
All that remains of her
Now is pure womanly.

Make no deep scrutiny
Into her mutiny
Rash and undutiful:
Past all dishonour,
Death has left on her
Only the beautiful.

The bleak wind of March
Made her tremble and shiver
But not the dark arch,
Or the black flowing river;
Mad from life's history,
Glad to death's mystery
Swift to be hurl'd –
Any where, any where
Out of the world!

Thomas Hood (1877)

The thought of suicide is a great comfort and helps me over many a bad night. Friedrich Nietzsche (1973)

25

Death Itself

Man that is born of woman hath but a short time to live, and is full
of misery. He cometh up and is cut down, like a flower; he fleeth as
it were a shadow . . . In the midst of life we are in death. The Book of
Common Prayer, Burial Service

> The place was rotten with dead; green clumsy legs
> High-booted, sprawled and grovelled along the saps
> And trunks, face downward, in the sucking mud,
> Wallowed like trodden sand-bags loosely filled;
> And naked sodden buttocks, mats of hair,
> Bulged, clotted heads slept in the plastering slime.
> Siegfried Sassoon (1961)

Dying Naturally

If you don't know how to die, don't worry; Nature will tell you
what to do on the spot, fully and adequately. She will do this job
perfectly for you; don't bother your head about it. Michel de Montaigne
(1958)

I am still sick and now and then I suspect that I am on the great
railway leading to the other side of the grave. At times this thought
is very painful, at other times I find in it the solace one experiences
on a train: the absence of responsibility in the face of a superior and
irresistible force. Prosper Mérimée (1874)

The Angel of Death speaks: 'I do not like your priests. It is they
who have taught men to fear my approach with their menace of

eternity and their flaming hell. It is they who have torn the wings from my shoulders and disfigured my friendly face and turned me into a hideous skeleton to wander from house to house, scythe in hand, like a thief in the night and dance to their *Danse Macabre* in the frescoes on their cloister walls hand in hand with their saints and their damned. I have nothing to do either with their heaven or with their hell. I am a Natural Law.' Axel Munthe (1949)

When I was a child growing up in Middle Georgia in the forties and fifties, people still died of old age . . . Some years ago, as an adult, I accompanied my mother to visit a very old neighbour who was dying a few doors down the street, and though she was no longer living in the country, the country style lingered . . . I thought her dying one of the most reassuring events I'd ever witnessed. She was calm, she seemed ready, her affairs were in order. She was respected and loved. In short, Mrs Davis was having an excellent death. A week later, when she had actually died, I felt this all the more because she had left, in me, the indelible knowledge that such a death is possible. And that cancer and nuclear annihilation are truly obscene alternatives. Alice Walker (1988)

The Experience of Death

Until, at last, light
As smoke, they feel once more
The gravity of the sky
And learn to fall upwards.
Edward Lowbury (1990)

Vital spark of heavenly flame!
Quit, oh quit this mortal frame!
Trembling, hoping, lingering, flying,
Oh the pain, the bliss of dying!
Cease fond nature, cease thy strife,
And let me languish into life!

Hark! they whisper; angels say,
'Sister spirit come away!'
What is this absorbs me quite?
Steals my senses, shuts my sight,
Drowns my spirits, draws my breath?
Tell me, my soul, can this be death?

The world recedes, it disappears!
Heaven opens on my eyes! my ears
With sounds seraphic ring:
Lend, lend your wings! I mount! I fly!
O Grave! where is thy victory?
O Death! where is thy sting?

Alexander Pope (1751)

And all at once it became clear to him that what had been oppressing him and would not go away was suddenly dropping away on one side, on two sides, on ten sides, on all sides. He felt full of pity for [his family], he must do something to make it less painful for them; release them and release himself from this suffering. 'How right and how simple,' he thought. 'And the pain?' he asked himself. 'What has become of it? Where are you, pain?'

He began to watch for it.

'Yes, here it is. Well, what of it? Let the pain be.'

'And death? Where is it?'

He searched for his former habitual fear of death and did not find it. 'Where is it? What death?' There was no fear because there was no death either.

In place of death there was light.

'So that's what it is!' he suddenly exclaimed aloud. 'What joy!'

To him all this happened in a single instant, and the meaning of that instant suffered no change thereafter. For those present his agony lasted another two hours. There was a rattle in his throat, a twitching of his wasted body. Then the gasping and the rattle came at longer and longer intervals.

'It's all over!' said someone near him.

He caught the words and repeated them in his soul. 'Death is over,' he said to himself. 'It is no more.'

He drew in a breath, stopped in the midst of a sigh, stretched out and died. Leo Tolstoy (1960)

Those who have the strength and the love to sit with a dying patient in the *silence that goes beyond words* will know that this moment is neither frightening or painful, but a peaceful cessation of the functioning of the body. Watching a peaceful death of a human being reminds us of a falling star; one of a million lights in a vast sky that flares up for a brief moment only to disappear into the endless night for ever. To be a therapist to a dying patient makes us aware of the uniqueness of each individual in this vast sea of humanity. Elizabeth Kubler-Ross (1979)

Life after Death

The Grave is Heaven's golden Gate,
And rich and poor around it wait.
William Blake (1977)

I'll die young but it's like kissing God. Lenny Bruce

Man is a being beyond time and beyond space who is conscious of himself in the conditions of space and time. One should conquer the fear of death, and when you cease to fear it, you cease to serve yourself as mortal, and you will serve an immortal God from whom you came and to whom you are going. Leo Tolstoy (1960a)

You purchase pain with all that joy can give,
And die of nothing but a rage to live.
Alexander Pope (1751)

Life Goes On

Earth must go back to earth: then life by all
Like crops is harvested.
Euripides

As the atoms are to the human unit, so the human units are to the
human whole. There is only One Man upon the earth; what we call
men are not individuals, but components; what we call death is but
the bursting of a cell. W. Winwood Reade (1872)

So looked my father at the last
Right in my soul, before he died,
Though words we spoke went heedless past
As London traffic-roar outside.

And now the same blue eyes I see
Look through me from a little son,
So questioning, so searchingly
That youthfulness and age are one.
John Betjeman (1970)

It all seems a bewildering chaos, a blind meaningless slaughter full of
confusion and blunders. At one moment Life, brandishing a new
weapon in its hand, advances victoriously, only to retire the next
moment, defeated by triumphant Death. It is not so. The battle is
regulated in its minutest details by an immutable law of equilibrium
between Life and Death. Wherever this equilibrium is upset by some
accidental cause, be it pestilence, earthquake or war, vigilant Nature
sets to work at once to readjust the balance, to call forth new beings
to take the place of the fallen. Compelled by the irresistible force of
a Natural Law, men and women fall into each other's arms, blindfolded
by lust, unaware that it is Death who presides over their mating, his
aphrodisiac in one hand, his narcotic in the other. Death, the giver of
Life, the slayer of Life, the beginning and the end. Axel Munthe (1949)

I am the family face
Flesh perishes, I live on,
Projecting trait and trace
Through time to times anon,
And leaping from place to place
Over oblivion.

The years-heired feature that can
In curve and voice and eye
Despise the human span
Of durance – that is I;
The eternal thing in man,
That heeds no call to die.

Thomas Hardy (1960)

26

The Sickness of the World

Fade far away, dissolve, and quite forget
What thou amongst the leaves hast never known,
The weariness, the fever, and the fret,
Here, where men sit and hear each other groan.
John Keats (1969)

Has there been another age that, knowing so clearly the right things to do, has so consistently done the wrong ones? Sir Laurens van der Post (1952)

The Writer Diagnoses the World's Sickness

Goethe has done his pilgrimage.
He took the suffering human race,
He read each wound, each weakness clear;
And stuck his finger on the place,
And said: Thou ailest here and here!

Ah! since dark days still bring to light
Man's prudence and man's fiery might,
Time may restore us in his course
Goethe's sage mind and Byron's force;
But where will Europe's latter hour
Again find Wordsworth's healing power.
Matthew Arnold (1853)

Thinking and writing to the very edge of insanity, and with some of his last pages even going over it, he read and interpreted the temperatures of his own mind; but by doing so he has drawn the fever chart of an epoch. Indeed, much of his work reads like the self-diagnosis of a desperate physician, who, suffering the disease on our behalf, comes to prescribe as a cure that we should form a new idea of health, and live by it. Erick Heller (1966), on Nietzsche

Art represents a process of self-regulation in the life of nations and epochs. C. G. Jung (1966a)

The Diagnosis

But all around me I see people afraid of slowing down, fearful of offending the production machines we work for. Arthur Frank (1991)

Our civilization exhausts us in some ways and leaves us underdeveloped in others. We are guided by materialistic aims, serving Mammon and becoming units of production and consumption, while soul and spirit are starving; the peak time for heart attacks is between eight and nine o'clock on Monday morning.

> Oh, born in days when wits were fresh and clear,
> And life ran gaily as the sparkling Thames;
> Before this strange disease of modern life,
> With its sick hurry, its divided aims,
> Its heads o'ertaxed, its palsied hearts, was rife.
> Matthew Arnold (1853)

> I wander thro' each charter'd street,
> Near where the charter'd Thames does flow,
> And mark in every face I meet
> Marks of weakness, marks of woe.

> In every cry of every man,
> In every infant's cry of fear,
> In every voice, in every ban,
> The mind-forged manacles I hear.
> William Blake (1794)

Your health is bound to be affected, if day after day you say the opposite of what you feel, if you grovel before what you dislike and rejoice at what brings you nothing but misfortune. Our nervous system isn't just a fiction, it's part of our physical body, and our soul exists in space and is inside us, like the teeth in our mouth. It can't be forever violated with impunity. Boris Pasternak (1995)

The great malady of the twentieth century, implicated in all of our troubles and affecting us individually and socially, is loss of soul. When soul is neglected, it doesn't just go away; it appears symptomatically in obsessions, addictions, violence, and loss of meaning. Our temptation is to isolate these symptoms or to try to eradicate them one by one; but the root problem is that we have lost our wisdom about the soul, even our interest in it. We have today few specialists of the soul to advise us when we succumb to moods and emotional pain, or when as a nation we find ourselves confronting a host of threatening evils. Thomas Moore (1992)

One wonders what will become of a society in which certain forms of suffering are avoided gratuitously, in keeping with middle-class ideals. I have in mind a society in which a marriage that is perceived as unbearable quickly and smoothly ends in divorce; after divorce no scars remain; relationships between generations are dissolved as quickly as possible, without a struggle, without a trace; periods of mourning are 'sensibly' short; with haste the handicapped and sick are removed from the house and the dead from the mind. If changing marriage partners happens as quickly as trading in an old car for a new one, then the experience one had in the unsuccessful relationship remains unproductive. From suffering nothing is learned and nothing is to be learned. Dorothee Solle (1975)

progress is a comfortable disease. e. e. cummings (1968)

The Present Treatment isn't Working

I will lift up mine eyes unto the pills. Almost everyone takes them, from the humble aspirin to the multicoloured, king-sized three deckers, which put you to sleep, wake you up, stimulate you and soothe you all in one. It is an age of pills. Malcolm Muggeridge (1962)

> . . . Consider, you,
> Whose rough hands manipulate
> The fine bones of a sick culture,
> What areas of that infirm body
> Depend solely on a poet's cure.
>
> R. S. Thomas (in Downie, 1995)

After diagnosing these communal sicknesses, the work of artists and writers is to offer treatment in the form of nourishment for soul and spirit. This is an alternative to alcohol, tranquillizers, antidepressants, etc., which only lead to dependency and the chemical control of unfulfilled lives. As a civilization, where are we heading when we need increasing amounts of drugs of one sort or another to control pain and create pleasure?

Is that the consequence of leaving your body to science? Of assuming that another pill, another drug, another car, another pocket-sized home-movie station, DNA transfer, or the complete freedom of choice that five hundred TV channels must bring will make everything all right? Will soothe the nagging pain in the heart that the latest laser scan refuses to diagnose? The doctor's surgery is full of men and women who do not know why they are unhappy.

Take this, says the doctor, 'You'll soon feel better.' They do feel better, because little by little, they cease to feel anything at all. Jeannette Winterson (1995)

Increasingly stronger stimuli are needed to provide people in an anaesthetic society with any sense of being alive. Drugs, violence and horror remain the only stimuli that can still elicit an experience of self. Widespread pain-killing increases the demand for painful excitation. Ivan Illich (1975)

In order to measure the extent to which modern life places a burden upon the nerves of the human being, we need only go back and consider life as it was a hundred or a hundred and fifty years ago. There was then no radio or cinema or telephone, no great cities with their continuous noise . . . There were also no industries alienated from nature, no mechanization of daily life. There was no craze for speed, no journalism to drive people from place to place in search of ever-new sensations, to say nothing of the flood of printed matter which inundates the present world.

... This pressure and tension may not be fully grasped in our consciousness, yet it does have an effect on our bodily functions ... At first we feel this only as tiredness ... Already today a complete regeneration is no longer possible, and this is the reason why most people have a certain craving for holidays. They live from one weekend to the next, are always tired and constantly feel the need for more and more stimulants, so that, in the long run, the situation can only grow worse. Dr Margarethe Hauschka (1984)

The soul is subject to health and disease, just as the body is. The health and disease of both ... undoubtedly depends on beliefs and custom, which are peculiar to mankind. Wherefore I call senseless beliefs and degenerate customs ... diseases of humanity. Maimonides (1963)

Insanity in individuals is something rare – but in groups, nations, and epochs it is the rule. Friedrich Nietzsche (1886)

Don't need a shot of heroin to cure my disease,
Don't need a shot of turpentine, only bring me to my knees,
Don't need a shot of codeine to help me to repent,
Don't need a shot of whiskey, help me be president,
I need a shot of love.
Doctor can you hear me? I need some Medicaid.
I seen the kingdoms of the world and it's making me feel afraid.
Bob Dylan (1981a)

A desperate disease requires a dangerous remedy. Guy Fawkes

PART III

GRANT US HEALTH WE PRAY —

THE MYSTERIES OF HEALING

Sick people sometimes raise their hopes to the spiritual world when no other help is at hand. So the final part of the book looks at illness from this perspective. Even when it is a last resort, a spiritual perspective can open up new and rewarding ways to approach health, illness and life itself.

> When I lie within my bed,
> Sick in heart and sick in head,
> And with doubts discomforted,
> Sweet spirit, comfort me!
> Robert Herrick (1648)

. . . when pain is to be borne, a little courage helps more than much knowledge, a little human sympathy more than much courage, and the least tincture of the love of God more than all. C. S. Lewis (1976)

I take upon myself the burden of all suffering, I am resolved to do so, I will endure it. I do not turn or run away, do not tremble, am not terrified, nor afraid, do not turn back or despond.

The whole world of living beings I must rescue, from the terrors of birth, of old age, of sickness, of death and rebirth . . . Vajradhvaja Sutra

He has borne our diseases and carried our sorrows . . . with his pain we are healed. Isaiah liii, 2−4

27

Mysticism: Beyond Health and Illness

Eastern religion and meditation appeal to us in the West because they have something which we lack. This is a mystic awareness of the continuity underlying the highs and lows of life. This continuity is now making a surprising appearance in Western science, in the form of chaos and complexity theory, where links are discovered between apparently unconnected events. Thus the mystic, and sometimes the scientist, sense an invisible background which binds our lives together. In this chapter we see how this relates to health and illness.

The Soul in the World

Call the world, if you please, the vale of soul-making. Then you will find out the use of the world. John Keats (1958)

The cycles of life include all the seasons of dark and light, fortune and misfortune. Resisting any of them is resisting the flow of life. By flowing with life, and learning that winter always leads to spring, we become wise, start to develop mystic consciousness and nourish our souls. Our souls then grow large enough to contain both the good times and the bad.

To everything there is a season, and a time to every purpose under heaven: a time to be born, and a time to die; a time to plant and a time to reap . . . a time to weep, and a time to laugh; a time to mourn, and a time to dance. Ecclesiastes iii, 1–4

> Till the blind mute soul get speech again and eyesight,
> Man may worship not the light of life within.
> A. C. Swinburne

And a woman spoke, saying, Tell us of Pain. And he said:

Your pain is the breaking of the shell that encloses your
understanding.

Even as the stone of the fruit must break, that its heart may stand
in the sun, so must you know pain.

And could you keep your heart in wonder at the daily miracles of
life, your pain would not seem less wondrous than your joy;

And you would accept the seasons of your heart, even as you have
always accepted the seasons that pass over your fields.

And you would watch with serenity through the winters of your
grief.

Much of your pain is self-chosen.

It is the bitter potion by which the physician within you heals
your sick self.

Therefore trust the physician, and drink his remedy in silence and
tranquillity:

For his hand, though heavy and hard, is guided by the tender hand
of the Unseen. Kahlil Gibran (1926)

Until the soul has got what it wants it must fall ill again.
James Hillman (1964)

The Paradoxes of Life

We are now entering into the area of life governed by paradox, where things
turn out to be not what they seem, and to have unpredictable effects.
Contradictory experiences can reveal that an unexpected unity lies behind
them. When our minds can entertain opposites, consciousness is extended.

You never know what is enough unless you know what is more
than enough. William Blake (1793)

As the eagle was killed by the arrow winged with his own feather,
so the hand of the world is wounded by its own skill. Helen Keller (1951)

Paradoxes of Healing

Paradoxically, we find that some writers say that illness can lead to wisdom.

Said one oyster to a neighbouring oyster, 'I have a very great pain within me. It is heavy and round, and I am in distress.'

And the other oyster replied with haughty complacence, 'Praise be to the heavens and to the sea, I have no pain within me. I am well and whole both within and without.'

At that moment a crab was passing by and heard the two oysters, and he said to the one who was well and whole both within and without, 'Yes, you are well and whole; but the pain that your neighbour bears is a pearl of exceeding beauty.' Kahlil Gibran (1932)

Health and illness are not so different. In the best moments of my illnesses I have been most whole. In the worst moments of my health I am sick. Where should I live? Health and illness, wellness and sickness perpetually alternate as foreground and background. Each exists only because of the other and can only alternate with its other. There is no rest in either word. In 'health' there can only be fear of illness, and in 'illness' there is only discontent at not being healthy. In recovery I seek not health but a word that has no opposite . . . Arthur Frank (1991)

To be sure, health is the only admissible ideal, to which . . . I consider a man has a right to aspire; but when health is given immediately to a human being, it hides half the world from him. Jacques Rivière

'Joy and Pain are Woven Fine'

Suffering and happiness are woven together in the course of our lives, and the resulting tapestry benefits the soul:

> Joy and pain are woven fine,
> A clothing for the soul divine.
> Under every grief and pine,
> Runs a thread of silken twine.
> This is right it must be so,

Man is made for joy and woe
And when this we rightly know
Safely through the world we go.

William Blake (1803)

Pleasure and pain are represented as twins, as though they were joined together, for there is never the one without the other . . . They are made with their backs turned to each other. They are made growing out of the same trunk because they have one and the same foundation, for the foundation of pleasure is labour with pain, and the foundations of pain are vain and lascivious pleasures. Leonardo da Vinci

I said to my soul, be still, and let the dark come upon you
Which shall be the darkness of God. As, in a theatre,
The lights are extinguished, for the scene to be changed . . .
So the darkness shall be the light, and the stillness the dancing.

T. S. Eliot (1944)

28

The Blessing in the Wound

My condition forged a link with things elemental – with the seasons, with the sun, and with my mother. John Updike (1989)

The Value of the Wound

In this book the word wound is used to mean an injury to the soul. When the experience of illness makes us attend to this wound we become more human and more compassionate, and something of value is taking place in our inner lives.

Was not my sly strength, my insistent specialness, somehow linked to my psoriasis? Might it not be the horrible badge of whatever in me was worth honouring? Only psoriasis could have taken a very average little boy, and furthermore a boy who loved the average, the daily, the safely hidden and made him into a prolific, adaptable, ruthless enough writer. What was my creativity, my relentless need to produce but a parody of my skin's overproduction? Was not my thick literary skin which shrugged off rejection slips and patronizing reviews by the sheaf, a superior version of my poor vulnerable own, and my shamelessness on the page a distraction from my real shame? . . . Dualism, indeed, such as existed between my skin and myself, appeared to me the very engine of the human. And with my changeable epiderm came a certain transcendent optimism; like a snake I shed many skins. John Updike (1989)

Why do you want to shut out of your life any agitation, any pain, any melancholy, since you really do not know what these states are working upon you? Why do you want to persecute yourself with the question whence all this may be coming and whither it may be bound? If there is anything morbid in your processes, just remember that sickness is the means by which an organism frees itself of foreign matter; so one must just help it to be sick, to have its whole sickness, and break out with it, for that is its purpose. Rainer Maria Rilke (1954)

Illness often takes on the disguise of love, and plays the same odd tricks. It invests certain faces with divinity, sets us to wait, hour after hour, with pricked ears for the creaking of a stair, and wreathes the faces of the absent (plain enough in health, Heaven knows) with a new significance, while the mind concocts a thousand legends and romances about them for which it has neither time nor taste in health. Virginia Woolf (1967)

The Blessing in the Wound

The well of our happiness is deepened by our suffering. Kahlil Gibran (1926)

Illness can be a blessing in disguise if it makes us more compassionate and more spiritual. In our illnesses we can find lost parts of ourselves asking for rehabilitation. This idea lies behind the mythology about the blessing in the wound – through the wound we can become more whole.

Don't turn your head, keep looking at the wounded place. That's where the light enters you. Rumi (sound recording)

I have heard the tradition said this way: 'When you die, you meet the Old Hag, and she eats your scars. If you have no scars she will eat your eyeballs, and you will be blind in the next world.' That story moves awfully fast but it certainly defends the value of scars. If one has no scars one becomes blind in the next world, but perhaps the man without scars is blind also in the imaginative world. Robert Bly (1991)

People too healthy, too determined to jog, too muscular, may use their health to prevent the soul from entering. They leave no door. Through the perfection of victory they achieve health, but the soul enters through the hole of defeat. Robert Bly (1991)

She knelt beside the corpse and held the bowl at the gushing wound.

When it brimmed with blood she held the cup to the dead body's lips. The dead mouth was made to drink. Alice was filled with primitive revulsion at the sight until she saw how the bluish tinge of the flesh was changing. A pearly suffusion of light was returning there. It was like watching dawn. Lindsay Clarke (1994)

Kissing the Beast: The Redemption of Disease

Just as we have to go through the winter to reach the joys of spring, so a profound healing can be found by going into the disease until a turning-point comes.

One thing that comes out in myths is that at the bottom of the abyss comes the voice of salvation. The black moment is the moment when the real message of transformation is going to come. At the darkest moment comes the light. Joseph Campbell

When we embrace all that we are, even the evil, the evil in us is transformed. When the diverse living energies of the human system are harmonized, the present bloody face of the world will be transformed into an image of the face of God. Andrew Bard Schmookler (1984)

Likely, diseases are the stimulus and the most interesting subject for our meditation and activity . . . Only we know little the art of using them.

Medicine must transform itself into the doctrine of the art of living.

Disease should be considered as bodily madness and, partially, as fixed ideas.

Life is a malady of the spirit, since in it one hopes with passion . . . Death is the principle that makes our life romantic. Death is – Life. Through death life is reinforced.

Every disease is a musical problem, healing is a musical solution.

If a man began to love disease or sorrow, the most exciting pleasure would penetrate him.

Poetry is the great art of constructing transcendental sanity. Therefore the poet is a transcendental physician.

Could disease not be a means of higher synthesis? Novalis

Pain is a holy angel who shows treasure to man which otherwise remains forever hidden. Adalbert Stifler

The sickness of the body may prove the health of the soul. Proverb

The only true wisdom lives far from mankind, out in the great loneliness, and it can be reached only through suffering. Igiugaruk (Eskimo) saying

Disease is the spirit attempting to reorganize its domain in this world. Malidoma Patrice Some (1995)

In order to pull us up and help us travel, messenger after messenger comes from the source of existence:

Every heartache and suffering that enters your body and heart pulls you by the ear to the promised Abode. Rumi (sound recording)

Between God and his servant are just two veils; all other veils become manifest from these two: health and wealth.

He who is healthy says, 'Where is God? I don't know and I don't see.' As soon as he begins to suffer he says, 'Oh God! Oh God!' He begins sharing his secrets with Him and talking to Him. So you see that health was his veil and God was hidden under his pain.

So long as man has riches, he gathers together all the means of achieving his desires. Night and day he busies himself with them. But as soon as he loses his wealth his ego weakens and he turns round about God. Rumi (sound recording)

When you have reached the lips of the great devourer you are staring into the jaws of creation. Normandi Ellis (1988)

29

Creativity and Illness

To *perceive* tragedy is to wring from it beauty and truth. Richard Selzer (1982)

The Wounded Writer and the Need to Write

It is a mistake to assume that creative writing arises when the writer has found solutions to the problems of life. Rather it comes when the writer feels the problem acutely, longing for an answer, and puts that experience into words. Thus writers are only healed of soul-sickness to the extent that they can feel the sickness and give voice to it. Every person has to find their own way of healing their soul: for writers it is writing. The anguish has to be expressed – in being creative the writer is attempting self cure.

No writer writes out of having found the answer to the problem; he writes rather out of his having the problem and *wanting* a solution. The solution consists not of a resolution. It consists of the *deeper and wider dimension of consciousness to which the writer is carried by virtue of his wrestling with the problem.* Rollo May (1969)

The need to express oneself in writing springs from a maladjustment to life, or from an inner conflict, which . . . man cannot resolve in action. André Maurois

One purpose of art, and the beauty which is its inspiration, is to counteract this experience of insignificance. Rollo May (1985)

Someone asked me why a surgeon would write . . . It is to search for some meaning in the ritual of surgery, which is at once murderous, painful, healing and full of love. Richard Selzer (1977)

Disease may well have been the ground
In full for that creative urge,
Creation was my body's purge,
Creating I've grown sane and sound.

Heinrich Heine (1967)

Writing is a form of therapy; I sometimes wonder how all those who do not write, compose or paint can manage to escape the madness, the melancholia, the panic fear which is inherent in the human situation.
Graham Greene

Painting is an attempt to come to terms with life. George Tooker

One day walking round Tavistock Square I made up, as I sometimes make up my books, *To The Lighthouse* (1927) in a great, apparently involuntary rush. One thing burst into another. Blowing bubbles out of a pipe gives the feeling of the rapid crowd of ideas and scenes which blew out of my mind, so that my lips seemed syllabling of their own accord as I walked. What blew the bubbles? Why then? I have no notion. But I wrote the book very quickly; and when it was written, I ceased to be obsessed by my mother. I no longer hear her voice; I do not see her. I suppose that I did for myself what psychoanalysts do for their patients. I expressed some very long felt and deeply felt emotion. And in expressing it I explained it and then laid it to rest.
Virginia Woolf (1967)

Those who have become eminent in philosophy, politics, poetry and the arts have all had tendencies towards melancholia. Socrates

Sometimes [the writer] can sneak an impending depression on to a character, 'and if you're very quick you can walk away and it'll stay with them'. Glynn Brown (1997)

'Physician to All Men'

What benefits can thou do, or all thy tribe
To the great world? Thou art a dreaming thing;
A fever of thyself . . .
                        Surely not all
Those melodies sung into the world's ear
Are useless: sure a poet is a sage;
A humanist, Physician to all men.

John Keats (1819)

If written words are medicines for their writers, are they also effective for others? *The Unquiet Grave* is an account of the depression of its author. It was written during a personal crisis which coincided with the Second World War. If the author writing of his own suffering expresses the pain of everyone, then the healing is shared. The writer becomes a healer.

As a signal of distress from one human being to another *The Unquiet Grave* went unanswered, but the suffering was alleviated. As a demonstration of the power of words, however, of the obsessional impetus in an aesthetic form to fulfil its destiny, the work was an object-lesson. All grief, once made known to the mind, can be cured by the mind, the manuscript proclaimed; the human brain, once it is fully functioning, as in the making of a poem, is outside time and place and immune from sorrow. '*La pensée console de tout.*' If *The Unquiet Grave*, therefore, should leave an impression of being morbid and gloomy then its intention has not been fulfilled. Cyril Connolly (1944)

Words are the physicians of a mind diseased. Aeschylus (1976)
Songs soothe with their touch. Pindar

Keats: Doctor and Poet

Keats and Chekhov both had medical training as well as being writers. All writers have been on the other side of the doctor's desk, as patients. It is in their articulation of the sufferings and the joys shared by all that they speak most powerfully. They are 'wounded healers' who heal others through enlightened knowledge of their own souls. Paradoxically, their weaknesses become their strengths.

Keats's short life was packed with suffering. Did the death of both his parents while he was still at school, and of his brother not much later, give him the urge to heal? He went on to do a medical training, but by the age of twenty-one he gave up medicine and devoted himself entirely to poetry. Keats wrote that he felt 'obliged to write to ease myself of the horror of my dying brother'. He died of TB at the age of twenty-five; near to death he wrote that he was the victim of his own passionate nature:

If I had any chance of recovering, this passion would kill me. John Keats (1969), writing from Italy to a friend

He was victim of his own passion and creativity, but thereby became 'physician to all men'.

Alchemy: The Treasure Buried in Suffering

The way in which artistic activity can feed the soul and transform suffering relates to the alchemical tradition. The alchemists' transformation of lead into gold is about changing what is raw and crude into something precious. One can turn this idea round – what is raw and crude then becomes essential to the creation of beauty, and illness becomes the raw material for healing. Illness is the grit which compels the oyster to create pearls. We can think of the deafness of Beethoven. This personal tragedy ended his career as a pianist and made him become a composer. So Beethoven's suffering did have its surprising benefits. Surely the power of his work springs partly from the torment a musician must endure when he loses his hearing.

The depressive and the exalted states of the artist, illness and health, are by no means sharply divided from each other . . . In illness, as it were under the lee of it, elements of health are at work, and elements of illness, working genius like, are carried over into health . . . Genius is a form of vital power deeply experienced in illness, creating out of illness, through illness creative. Thomas Mann (1992)

For the sake of a single verse . . . one must be able to think back to roads in unknown regions . . . to days of childhood that are still unexplained . . . to childhood illnesses that so strangely begin with such a number of profound and grave transformations, to days in rooms withdrawn and quiet . . . Rainer Maria Rilke (1975)

Craziness and Creativity

Figures of mad genius like Van Gogh the painter, or half-crazy drunken poets, are part of our popular mythology. Genius and madness are not so far apart, it seems, and some of the most creative people can slip from one to the other. Guy de Maupassant is an example:

He would often rush up the steps of Avenue de Villiers to sit down in a corner of my room looking at me in silence with that morbid fixity of his eyes I knew so well. Often he used to stand for minutes staring at himself in the mirror over the mantelpiece as if he was looking at a stranger. One day he told me that while he was sitting at his writing-table hard at work on his new novel he had been greatly surprised to see a stranger enter his study notwithstanding the severe vigilance of his valet. The stranger had sat down opposite him at the writing-table and began to dictate to him what he was about to write. He was just going to ring for François to have him turned out when he saw to his horror that the stranger was himself. Axel Munthe (1949)

A Baudelaire, even better a Dostoevsky, who in thirty years, between their epileptic and other crises, create something of which not a single paragraph could have been accompanied by a whole line of a thousand merely healthy artists. Marcel Proust

The Healing Power of Story and Myth

The healing power of story and poetry is underestimated. TV soap operas have millions of faithful viewers, so the attraction of stories is still strong, but the healing potential is neglected. By means of a story we can relate ourselves and our suffering to a human drama which spans centuries. Versions of this drama appear in the Greek myths, in Shakespeare and in poems the writers never show to anyone. The comfort of reading and writing these can release a troubled mind, and help restore body and soul.

In the oldest sense, storytelling is a healing art. It reconciles us to our anxieties and makes it possible for us to master them. It assures us that our values are right and that our lives will continue, and teaches us what we must do to find ourselves. It connects us to the archetypes which guide us through life.

In primitive societies stories were part of the rituals which initiated people into each successive passage of life, from birth to death. At each transition an old self was left behind, a new identity assumed, and a new role in society accepted. Religion no longer has the power to smooth these transitions for us. We have few rituals now, but many stories to teach us what lies ahead. Celia Brayfield (1996)

Wounds need to be expanded into air, lifted up on ideas our ancestors knew, so that the wound ascends through the roof of our parents' house and we suddenly see how our wound (seemingly so private) fits into a great and impersonal story. Robert Bly (1991)

In Ancient Egypt if someone was bitten by a snake then he was taken to a temple of Ra the Sun God and told the story of that god's daily struggle against Apep, the serpent of darkness. John Cowper Powys (1933)

In dealing with stories, we are handling archetypal energy, which is a lot like electricity. It can animate and enlighten, but in the wrong place and wrong time and wrong amount, like any medicine, it can have no desired effect. Clarissa Pinkola Estes (1992)

... myth wells up spontaneously within the mind according to some involuntary processes which shape the brain itself, the foetus within the womb, and the molecular pattern of the elements. For myth is the complex of images eventually assumed by all involuntary imagination, since, left to itself, imagination takes on a structure in the same manner as the body and the brain. Alan W. Watts (1968)

I encourage people to do their own mining of story, for the scraped knuckles, the sleeping on cold ground, the groping in the dark and the adventures on the way are worth everything. There must be a little spilled blood on every story if it is to carry the medicine.

I hope you will go out and let stories happen to you, and that you will work them, water them with your blood and tears and your laughter till they bloom, till you yourselves burst into bloom. Then you will see what medicines they make, and where and when to apply them.

... one is enabled in the story, in the medicine, by the amount of self that one is willing to sacrifice and put into it. Clarissa Pinkola Estes (1992)

30

The Shamanic Way of Health

The witch doctor succeeds for the same reason all the rest of us succeed. Each patient carries his own doctor inside him. They come to us not knowing this truth. We are at our best when we give the doctor who resides within each patient a chance to go to work. Albert Schweitzer

The Shaman and the Soul

The shaman has always understood illness as soul-sickness. Through his or her own suffering, and consequent experience of the world of the soul, the shaman becomes qualified to heal others.

Soul loss is regarded as the gravest diagnosis, being seen as a cause of illness and death. Yet it is not referred to at all in modern Western medical books. It is becoming increasingly clear that what the shaman refers to as soul loss – that is injury to the inviolate core that is the essence of the person's being – does manifest in despair, immunological damage, cancer, and a host of other very serious disorders. It seems to follow the demise of relationships with loved ones, career, or other significant attachments. Jeanne Achterberg

Everything that concerns the soul and its adventure here on earth and in the beyond, is the exclusive province of the shaman. Through his own initiatory and pre-initiatory experiences, he knows the drama of the human soul, its instability, its precariousness; in addition he knows the forces that threaten it and the regions to which it can be carried away. Mircea Eliade (1989)

The evil spirits carry the future shaman's soul to the underworld and there shut it up in a house for three years (only one year for those who will become lesser shamans). Here the shaman undergoes his initiation. The spirits cut off his head, which they set aside (for the candidate must watch his dismemberment with his own eyes), and cut him into small pieces, which are then distributed to the spirits of the various diseases. Only by undergoing such an ordeal will the future shaman gain the power to cure. Mircea Eliade (1989)

The Shaman's Cures

We no longer believe that disease is caused by evil spirits. However, when we take antibiotics we may still feel a trace of the satisfaction of 'casting out devils', even though the devils are invading micro-organisms.

Shamanic healing rituals often have the function of raising unconscious conflicts and resistances to a conscious level, where they can develop freely and find a resolution. This, of course, is also the basic dynamic of modern psychotherapies, and indeed there are numerous similarities. Shamans used therapeutic techniques such as group sharing, psychodrama, dream analysis, suggestion, hypnosis, guided imagery and psychedelic therapy for centuries before they were rediscovered by modern physiologists. Fritjof Capra (1983)

Trance and deep hypnosis are healing. They liberate us from the machinery of thought; they purify our consciousness of its compulsive, incessant inner dialogue, of its relentless, ongoing evaluating and judging . . . Trance means healing through inner recuperation from the unending stream of external stimuli, from complex thinking, from complicated emotions. Holger Kalweit (1992)

I remember the blind healer in the village who worked at night and slept during the day. The man was so skilled at conversing with trees that he baffled even his fellow medicine men with his spectacular talent for obtaining medicine from nature. His consultations always ended in the middle of the night. Then the patient was ordered to follow him into the bush. There he would speak to Mother Nature in a strange language, giving her a list of illnesses. She would respond in a buzzing language, telling him which plants he needed to gather.

Then the vegetal world would awake in the middle of darkness, every tree and every plant – all speaking to the man at once. For the witness it was gibberish, but for the blind healer it made sense. He would translate, telling each patient that such and such a tree said his fruit, dried and pounded and then mixed with salted water and drunk, would take care of the disease in question . . .

The healer was totally dependent on this dialogue with the vegetal in his work. He often said that the vegetal world was better than the human one because it knew more than we did, and because it is of a finer species than we are. The vegetal world can get along without us, but we cannot progress without the help of the vegetal. Malidoma Patrice Some (1995)

When I work with the hand power it is just like when you cast for fish and the fish tug on your bait – it feels like it would with the fish pulling on your line – that's what it is like. The pain sitting somewhere inside the person feels like it is pulling the hand towards itself – you can't miss it . . .

There is a doctoring power in my throat. Here somewhere in my throat the power sits . . . When I first doctored with my throat, it was for a young woman. When I treated her and sucked the disease out, something like a bubble came up out of my throat; just as it would if you blew up a big balloon, that is how it came from my mouth . . . Ever since then I've been sucking diseases out . . . I spit out the dead disease. Essie Parrish

Healing does not come from the visible world, but from the invisible shadow world. This is the world to which our subtle-material body belongs, our energy body; its visible form is the physical body. This shadow land is the homeland of shamans, where they 'operate', give 'shots' and 'medicine'. We know little of this land, the 'quantum realm of the holy'. The things shamans say to us about it are metaphors, images that have been run through the brain and filtered through it. Holger Kalweit (1992)

There is an eternal vital correspondence between our blood and the sun, there is an eternal vital correspondence between our nerves and the moon. If we get out of harmony with the sun and the moon, then both turn into great dragons of destruction against us. The sun is a great source of blood vitality, it streams strength to us. But once we resist the sun and say it is a mere ball of gas, then the very streaming vitality of sunshine turns into a subtle disintegrative force in us and undoes us. The same with the moon, the planets, the great stars. They are either our makers or our undoers. When I hear modern people complain of being lonely then I know what has happened . . . What we lack is cosmic life, the sun in us and the moon in us. We can't get the sun in us by lying naked like pigs on a beach. The very sun that is bronzing us is inwardly disintegrating us – as we know later . . . We can only get the sun by a sort of worship, by going forth to worship the sun, worship that is felt in the blood. D. H. Lawrence (1995)

31

The Healing Mysteries of
Gods and Goddesses

To open to mystery is to acknowledge the body's true hungers, to seek for the Food and Water of Life that restore us when we hang on the gates of death. To open to mystery is to love the body, to marvel at its pleasures, to allow ourselves to fully feel its sensitivity to pain.
Starhawk (1987)

There are many hidden forces at work in our world. Sub-molecular forces shape the material world. Life-forces shape the trees and the fishes and our own bodies. Many names have been given to these powers in different parts of the world and through history. We may call them gods and goddesses and pray to them. Modern scientists speak of 'the implicate order', and similar phenomena. Perhaps all are referring to the same thing, for today mystery seems to have a place in science as well as religion.

The Gods and Goddesses of Disease

The art of medicine is my discovery. I am called Help-bringer throughout the world, and all the potency of herbs is known to me. Ovid (1995) as spoken by Apollo

There are mythological accounts of the origins of disease. One ancient Greek version is that Apollo and Artemis each fired six arrows at six men and women, thus planting diseases in the human race. The same gods and goddesses also offer healing. The mystery is that the disease and the healing come from the same source.

Tribal imagination has long grouped illnesses under the name of the ancestor or god who rules them. By digging down into the ground below any culture, we can find some system of tracing the shape of a disease to the particular style of a god, ancestor, or saint. Ultimately, the diseased person had to seek the cure in the temple or in the sacred ground of the god who claimed that disease and its victims. The victim of trouble or disease was seen to be in a complex condition. The old idea was that the 'afflicted were sacred' – not because they were better people but because they had been touched by a god. In touching the victim, you were touching one who had been touched by the god.

Part of the purpose of the affliction was to draw that soul to the service of that god, to introduce the individual to the ritual ground of that deity or ancestor. The ritual style of the particular deity indicated the way to withstand or relieve the affliction. All who survived the touch of the god became followers of the god. The symptom was the other world trying to break through . . . Michael Meade (1993)

Healing: A Gift from the Gods and Goddesses

The gods' and goddesses' gifts do not come easily: we have to search them out and we have to go through suffering to find them. Healing is bestowed on their terms, it seems.

The Babylonian superhero Gilgamesh, wearied by many adventures, goes in search of immortality to meet Uta-napishtim the Faraway, an immortal. Gilgamesh fails the test he is set and remains mortal, but the god grants him something:

So Uta-napishtim spoke . . . 'Gilgamesh, you came here a man wearied out, you have worn yourself out; what shall I give you to carry you back to your own country? Gilgamesh, I shall reveal a secret thing, it is a mystery of the gods that I am telling you. There is a plant that grows under the water, it has a prickle like a thorn, like a rose; it will wound your hands, but if you succeed in taking it, then your hand will hold that which restores his lost youth to a man.'

When Gilgamesh heard this he opened the sluices so that a sweet-water current might carry him out to the deepest channel; he tied heavy stones to his feet and they dragged him down to the water-bed. There he saw the plant growing; although it pricked him he took it in his hands; then he cut the heavy stones from his feet, and the sea carried him and threw him on to the shore. Gilgamesh said to Urshanabi the ferryman, 'Come here and see this marvellous plant. By its virtue a man may win back all his former strength. I will take it to Uruk of the strong walls; there I will give it to the old men to eat. Its name shall be "The Old Men are Young Again"; and at last I shall eat it myself and have back all my lost youth.' So Gilgamesh returned by the gate through which he had come, Gilgamesh and Urshanabi went together. They travelled their twenty leagues and then they broke their fast; after thirty leagues they stopped for the night.

Gilgamesh saw a well of cool water and he went down and bathed; but deep in the pool there was lying a serpent, and the serpent sensed the sweetness of the flower. It rose out of the water and snatched it away, and immediately it sloughed its skin and returned to the well. Then Gilgamesh sat down and wept, tears ran down his face, and he took the hand of Urshanabi; 'O Urshanabi, was it for this that I toiled with my hands, is it for this I have wrung out my heart's blood? For myself I have gained nothing; not I, but the beast of the earth has joy of it now. Already the stream has carried it twenty leagues back to the channels where I found it. I found a sign and now I have lost it.'
The Epic of Gilgamesh (1972)

And the leaves of the tree were for the healing of the nations.
Revelations xx, 2

Here an angel brings the healing:

He had quite simply come to her window and welcomed her, and she had gone to him, and he had healed her or whatever you want to call it. In a single moment she had recovered from her life. That was it! Her whole life had been a terrible sickness – she saw that now so clearly – and he had cured her of it. For ever would she remember the heat beneath those wings. No matter how cold she was ever to grow, she would be warmed by the memory of it . . . the Grace came, or whatever it was that leaped like a deer deep within her, moving in the quietest, most forestal parts of her, and changed her for ever.
Richard Selzer (1974)

Three instances are given in which the suppliant refuses to believe that what he has seen is a real vision of the saints, but declares it to be an evil fantasy, and therefore does not carry out the instructions conveyed to him. In each case the instructions of the saints bordered on the ridiculous, and this comic element may account for the incredulity with which the suppliant received the vision. One man who was suffering from headache was told to go to a certain door of the church and strike the first person whom he met. The order was given three times before he obeyed. A soldier met him and returned the blow by a heavy stroke of his stick on the man's head, thus curing him. Theodurus was told to swallow an asp, but he also refused to believe in the good faith of the vision. The third time the saints varied their command, and told him to eat whatever he found at the fountain. He did so, and in the cucumber which he found there was hidden an asp. He swallowed half without being aware of its presence, and it rid him of the poison. Mary Hamilton (1906)

Asclepius, Family and Friends

The Greek god Asclepius was one of the most venerated of gods, and his worship persisted for thousands of years, even after the birth of Christ. He was assisted by his family and friends: Hygeia deals with prevention of disease, Panacea with cure, and Telesphorus with convalescence. Healing at his temples was by invitation only (the invitations were delivered in the patients' dreams) – hence the large numbers of sick people waiting long outside the temple gates hoping to be admitted. The methods of healing involved 'temple sleep', snakes, rituals and moral guidance as well as medicines.

The god of healing, with all his train of abundant divinities, Hygeia, Panacea, and Telesphorus (god of convalescence) and the many others – kindly presences all of them, called into being solely to ease men's pain – may be thought of as dwelling somewhere between the gods above and men below ... to be at hand when men required their instant aid. Louis Dyer (1891)

[The healer] ought to be able to bring about love and reconciliation between the most antithetic elements in the body ... Our ancestor Asclepius knew how to bring love and concord to these opposites and he it was, as poets say and I believe, who founded our art. Plato (1995)

And silence
Had hardly fallen, when the god, all crested
With gold, in serpent form, uttered a warning,
Hissed terribly, a sign that he was coming,
And all the altars, all the doors, the pavement,
The roof of gold, the statue, shook and trembled.
Reared high, he stood there, and he gazed about him
With fiery eyes, and as the people shuddered,
The priest, in ceremonial head-dress, knew him,
Calling, 'The god! Behold the god! Bow down
To him in word and spirit, all who stand here!
That we may see his beauty as a blessing,
Here at his shrine.'
Ovid (1995)

Walk the length of the abaton; the sick are in their places, each upon his pallet. Here is one that cannot sleep. See how his breath rises and falls against some burden that presses upon it. At last, he dozes, only to awaken minutes later, unrefreshed. It is toward dawn. The night lamps flicker low, casting snaky patterns across the colonnade. Already the chattering swallows swoop in and out among the pillars. All at once the fitful eyes of the man cease their roving, for he sees between the candle lamp and the wall the shadow of an upraised serpent, a great yellow snake with upraised eyes. It slides closer. It is arched and godlike. It bends above him, swaying, the tongue and the lamplight flickering as one. Exultant, he raises himself upon one arm, and with the other, reaches out for the touch that heals. Richard Selzer (1982)

Divine Hygeia from the bending sky
Descends, listens to his piercing cry;
Assumes bright Digitalis' dress and air . . .
O'er him she waves her serpent wreathed wand,
Cheers with her voice and raises with her hand,
Warms with rekindling bloom his visage wan,
And charms the shapeless monster into man.
Erasmus Darwin (1789)

The Caduceus: The Healing Serpent

The serpent as a symbol initially represents whatever is feared and has to be cast out, which includes disease. Yet many schools of healing include serpents in their logos: here we have another mystery – an ambivalent and esoteric symbol, embracing both dark and light. The snake's magical powers are also demonstrated in its power to shed its skin, and thus renew itself.

The caduceus is a symbol of healing adopted by many healers and professional organizations. It has a snake (or sometimes two) coiled around a staff.

The two snakes of Mercury's caduceus are the two nerve channels, the ida and the pingala, which spiral around the central passageway of the spinal column, of Tantric Yoga. William Irwin Thompson (1981)

After a time a second snake crept out of the hole, and when it saw the other lying dead and cut in pieces, it went back, but soon came again with three green leaves in its mouth. Then it took the three pieces of the snake, laid them together as they fitted, and placed one of the leaves on each wound. Immediately the severed parts joined themselves together, the snake moved, and became alive again, and both of them hastened away together. Brothers Grimm (1995)

> Shedding off one more layer of skin,
> Keeping one step ahead of the persecutor within.
> Bob Dylan (1983a)

Celtic Gods and Goddesses of Healing

Deities of healing were found everywhere in the days when faith was strong. Despite their many different names, they were often remarkably similar in their methods. For the Celts, Diancecht and his family were the supreme healers of injury; Aengus Mac Og was healer of souls. Also of widespread importance were Bride (or Brighid) and Goibnin and there were many local divinities, often connected with springs. Diancecht restored slain Celtic warriors by immersing their bodies in holy wells and chanting healing incantations over them. Sulis is the great healing goddess of the springs in the city of Bath.

There is a story of Diancecht's son Miach doing a miraculous healing which Diancecht thought was wrong. Perhaps it is one of the first stories of interdisciplinary rivalry. Diancecht struck Miach. Miach healed himself. Diancecht struck again. And again Miach healed himself. Diancecht's third blow cut into his son's brain and Miach died. On his grave grew 365 herbs, one for each part of the musculo-skeletal system. However, Diancecht cast a spell which confused our knowledge of them.

> Bride went out
> One morning early,
> With her two horses;
> One broke its leg
> With much ado.
> What was apart
> She put together
> Bone to bone,
> Flesh to flesh,
> Sinew to sinew,
> Vein to vein;
> As she healed that
> May we heal this.
>
> Caitlin Matthews (1993)

This poem describes the healing power of a ring-shaped stone set in the ground in Cornwall:

> Men an Tol
> Through thee I crawl.
> Holed grey stone
> Knit the bone;
> Holed grey boulder
> Straighten the shoulder;
> Adder's lintel
> make me gentle;
> Hole of the rain
> Charm the migraine;
> Stone figure nought

Strengthen the heart;
Hole of the wind
Straighten the mind;
Nose-ring on rock-beast
Bring up harvest;
Ring of granite
Straighten the planet.

D. M. Thomas (1983)

Jacob's Struggle with the Angel

Among the Old Testament stories of illness there are the accounts of Job and his boils, and Jacob's struggle all night with an angel. Some people afflicted with illness have found such stories helpful, acting as a blessing on their own struggle. However, the last passage in this section shows how it is possible to explain these stories without recourse to magic:

Jacob's wrestling became a story I lived with as part of my personal mythology of illness. This is what it is to be ill: to wrestle through the long night, injured, and if you prevail until the sun rises, to receive a blessing. Through Jacob's story, illness became an adventure. Arthur Frank (1991)

The wrestling is a struggle but not a fight. Jacob wins not by defeating his darker side, but by realizing the other he is contesting shares the face of God. Jacob does not overcome his opponent; instead he finds divinity in him. The outcome of the wrestling match is twofold. Jacob leaves with a wound: 'The sun rose upon him and he halted upon his thigh.' He also gains a blessing: The servant of God also wins for himself the prize the trickster first stole, but perhaps the blessing is that now the two have become one. Wounded, Jacob becomes whole. Whole, he is renamed. Arthur Frank (1991)

Jacob sent his family, servants and cattle across the Jordan at Jabbok, where the river is narrow (Genesis xxxii, 22). He stayed alone on the opposite bank and struggled with an angel all night. When the angel found that he could not win, he touched Jacob in the crotch and Jacob's 'thigh was put out of joint'. The hip joint is so strong that dislocation is rare. There is, however, a form of anterior dislocation which may (rarely) be produced when a person embarking in a boat hesitates whether to stay on land or get in the boat. Margaret Lloyd Davies and T. A. Lloyd Davies (1993)

Christ: Wounded God and Wounded Healer

Christ is God become human, and through his human frame he channelled healing which originates in higher realms. He is a perfect example of the healing powers of gods and goddesses.

And it came to pass, when he was in a certain city, behold a man full of leprosy: who seeing Jesus fell on his face, and besought him, saying, Lord, if thou wilt, thou canst make me clean. And he put forth his hand and touched him, saying, I will: be thou clean. And immediately the leprosy departed from him. And he charged him to tell no man; but go, and shew thyself to the priest, and offer for thy cleansing, according as Moses commanded, for a testimony unto them. But so much the more went there a fame abroad of him; and great multitudes came together to hear, and to be healed by him of their infirmities. And he withdrew himself into the wilderness, and prayed. Luke v, 12–16

Jesus was distinctly shamanistic. He, too, talked with his spirits, as is exemplified in the story of the Temptations in the Wilderness and the frequent sojourns he spent alone in communion with God. Like the shamans, Jesus healed the sick and was on familiar terms with the denizens of the spiritual world. John A. Sanford (1977)

Creation implies a diffusing and distributing of power out of a centre, which in a sense is a sacrifice or self-elected wound on the part of the Creator. Sacrifice finds its ultimate expression in the crucifixion of Christ, for here God assumes manhood and suffers death for the purpose of redeeming mankind's fall. The cosmic drama, it seems, is built on wounding and the shedding of blood . . . Herbert Whone (1990)

The poison of evil and death comes into the world, into the heart of the First Adam, through the Serpent on the Tree. Healing comes through the Second Adam, Christ crucified on the Tree of the Cross . . .

Let us remember, also, the myth which identifies the Wood of their Cross with the staff or beam taken from the Tree of Eden, so that the

Cross which is *medicina mundi* is of the same tree which bore the fruit of knowledge, the poison of death. Alan W. Watts (1968)

I often wonder what would happen to the world if innocent people did not suffer so much. They are the ones who are interceding the whole time. Their innocence is so pleasing to God. By accepting suffering, they intercede for us. Mother Teresa

One patient had to leave our home to go to hospital. When I visited him he said to me, 'Mother Teresa, you are my friend. I want to talk to you alone.'

What did he say after twenty-five years of being away from God? 'When I get the terrible pain in my head, I share it with Jesus and suffer as He did when He was crowned with thorns. When I get the terrible pain in my back, I share it with Him when He was scourged at the pillar, and when I get the pain in my hands and feet, I share it with Him when He was nailed to the cross. I ask you to take me home. I want to die with you.'

I got permission and took him to our home, Gift of Love, and took him into the chapel. I never heard anyone talk to Jesus as this man talked to Him, so tenderly, so full of love. Three days later he died. Mother Teresa (1993)

The worst disease today is not leprosy; it is being unwanted, being left out, being forgotten. The greatest scourge is to forget the next person, to be so suffocated, so to say, with things that we have no time for the lonely Jesus – even a person in our own family who needs us.

Maybe if I had not picked up that one person dying on the street, I would not have picked up the thousands. Mother Teresa

In every infected, smelly laceration, I saw the wounds of Jesus. Paulo Coelho (1996)

32

Here's to Your Health!
Blessings and Prayers for Health

Ring out old shapes of foul disease.
Alfred Lord Tennyson (1850)

When we automatically say 'Good health' before drinking alcohol, perhaps we do not properly remember the time-honoured power of blessings and prayers. Faith is important in the effectiveness of these, and in our times faith is running low. But in spite of ourselves, our souls can still be moved by such things. If we reach into soul levels, as we find ourselves doing in a crisis, prayers and blessings have renewed power, and familiar words can take on a new meaning.

Christian Blessings and Prayers

O Mary, permit me this grace,
this crossing over,
although I am ugly,
submerged in my own past
and my own madness.
. . . O Mary, tender physician,
come with powders and herbs . . .
Anne Sexton (1967)

The Lord is my shepherd; I shall not want.
He maketh me to lie down in green pastures: He leadeth me beside
the still waters.

He restoreth my soul: He guideth me in the paths of righteousness
    for his name's sake.
Yea, though I walk through the valley of the shadow of death,
I will fear no evil; for thou art with me:
Thy rod and thy staff, they comfort me.

Psalm xxiii

Come unto me, all ye that labour and are heavy laden and I will
    give you rest.

Matthew xi, 28

Blessed are the poor in spirit: for theirs is the kingdom of heaven.
Blessed are they that mourn: for they shall be comforted.
Blessed are the meek: for they shall inherit the earth.

Matthew v, 3–5

Celtic Blessings and Prayers

Deep peace of the running wave to you,
Deep peace of the flowing air to you,
Deep peace of the quiet earth to you,
Deep peace of the shining stars to you;
May peace, may peace, may peace fill your soul;
May peace, may peace, may peace make you whole.

Celtic blessing

The knee that is stiff, O Healer, make pliant,
The heart that is hard make warm beneath Thy wing;
The soul that is wandering from thy path,
Grasp thou his helm and he shall not die.

Each thing that is foul cleanse thou early,
Each thing that is hard soften Thou with Thy grace,
Each wound that is working us pain,
O Best of Healers, make Thou whole!

Alexander Carmichael (1988); a Celtic prayer

A shade art thou in the heat,
A shelter art thou in the cold,
Eyes art thou to the blind,
A staff art thou to the pilgrim,
An island art thou at sea,
A fortress art thou on land,
A well art thou in the desert,
Health art thou to the ailing.

Alexander Carmichael (1988)

'Sweet Spirit Comfort Me'

Let neither grief, nor fear, nor boundless joy,
The peace and vigour of thy mind destroy.

Scevola de Sainte-Marthe

When I lie within my bed,
Sick in heart and sick in head,
And with doubts discomforted,
Sweet spirit comfort me!

When the house doth sigh and weep,
And the world is drowned in sleep,
Yet mine eyes the watch do keep,
Sweet spirit comfort me!

When the artless doctor sees
No one hope but of his fees,
And his skill runs on the lees,
Sweet spirit comfort me!

When his potion and his pill
Has, or none, or little skill,
Meet for nothing but to kill,
Sweet spirit comfort me!

When the passing bell doth toll,
And the Furies in a shoal
Come to fright a parting soul,
Sweet spirit comfort me!

When the tapers now burn blue,
And the comforters are few,
And that number more than true,
Sweet spirit comfort me!

When the priest his last hath pray'd,
And I nod to what is said,
'Cause my speech is now decay'd,
Sweet spirit comfort me!

Robert Herrick (1648)

May your suffering decrease
the misfortunes of your next birth, they said.
May the sum of evil
balanced in this unreal world
against the sum of good
become diminished by your pain.

Nissim Ezekiel (1982)

As this onion is peeled and thrown into the fire,
Consumed by the glowing fire God,
So may the ban, curse, pain and woe,
Sickness, groans, injury, sin, misdeed and transgression,
So may the sickness in my body, in my flesh, in my limbs
As this peeled onion, be consumed by the glowing Fire God.

Assyrian prayer

Sink down, sink down, sink deeper and more deep
Into eternal and primordial sleep.
Sink down, be still, forget and draw apart
Into the inner earth's most secret heart.
Drink of the waters of Persephone,

The secret well beside the sacred tree.
Waters of life and strength and inner light –
Eternal joy born from the deeps of night.
Then rise, made strong, with life and hope renewed,
Reborn from darkness and from solitude.
Blessed with the blessing of Persephone,
And secret strength of Rhea, Binah, Ge.
Dion Fortune (1989)

Earth cure me. Earth receive my woe. Rock strengthen me. Rock receive my weakness. Rain wash my sadness away. Rain receive my doubt. Sun make sweet my song. Sun receive the anger from my heart.
Nancy Wood (1972)

Away, melancholy,
Away with it, let it go.

Are not the trees green,
The earth as green?
Does not the wind blow,
Fire leap and the rivers flow?
Away melancholy.

The ant is busy
He carrieth his meat,
All things hurry
To be eaten or eat.
Away, melancholy.

Beaten, corrupted, dying
In his own blood lying
Yet heaves up an eye above
Cries, Love, love.
It is his virtue needs explaining,
Not his failing.
Stevie Smith (1985)

Health and Happiness to All

O Health! Health! The blessing of the rich! The riches of the poor!
Ben Jonson

> From being anxious, or secure,
> Dead clods of sadness, or light squibs of mirth,
> From thinking, that great courts immure
> All, or no happiness, or that this earth
> Is only for our prison framed,
> Or that thou art covetous
> To them whom thou lov'st, or that they are maimed
> For reaching this world's sweet, who seek thee thus,
> With all their might, Good Lord deliver us.
> John Donne (1971)

> Love, from its awful throne of patient power
> In the wise heart, from the last giddy hour
> Of dead endurance, from the slippery, steep,
> And narrow verge of crag-like agony, springs
> And folds over the world its healing wings.
> P. B. Shelley (1977)

> May your hands always be busy,
> May your feet always be swift,
> May you have a strong foundation
> When the winds of changes shift.
> May your heart always be joyful,
> May your song always be sung,
> May you stay forever young.
> Bob Dylan (1973, 1974)

> I rise this day
> With the life of heaven
> With the light of the sun
> With the radiance of the moon

With the splendour of fire
With the speed of lightning
With the breath of wind
With the depth of the sea
With the strength of earth
With the firmness of rock.

Hymn of St Patrick

If I live to be old, for I find I go down,
Let this be my fate. In a country town,
May I have a warm house, with a stone at the gate,
And a cleanly young girl, to rub my bald pate.
May I govern my passions with an absolute sway,
And grow wiser, and better, as my strength wears away,
Without gout or stone, by a gentle decay.

Walter Pope

By nature honest, by experience wise,
Healthy by temp'rance and by exercise,
His life, though long, to sickness passed unknown,
His death was instant, and without a groan.
O grant me thus to live and thus to die!
Who sprung from kings shall know less joy than I.

Alexander Pope (1751)

And here I cease to write but will not cease
To wish you live in health, and die in peace;
And ye our physicke rules that friendly read,
God grant that physicke you may never need.

Saleme School

Bibliography

Abse, Dannie, *White Coat, Purple Coat: Collected Poems 1948–1988*, Hutchinson, London, 1989

Aeschylus, *Complete Plays*, trans. Gilbert Murray, Allen & Unwin, London, 1976

Alcott, Louisa May, *Journal*, 1874

Anthony, Edward, *Every Dog Has His Day*, Watson Guptill Publications, New York, 1942

Arbuthnot, John, *Know Thyself*, 1734

Armstrong, Dr John, *The Art of Preserving Health*, II, 1744

Arnold, Matthew, *The Scholar Gypsy*, 1853
    New Poems, 1867

Auden, W. H., *Selected Poems*, Penguin Books, London, 1967

Auld, Philip, *Honour a Physician*, Hollis & Carter, London, 1959

Austen, Jane, *Persuasion*, 1818

Bach, Dr Edward, *Collected Writings of Edward Bach*, ed. Julian Barnard, Bach Educational Programme, Hereford, 1987

Bacon, Sir Francis, *The Advancement of Learning*, II, 1605

Balzac, Honoré de, *Selected Short Stories*, trans. Sylvia Raphael, Penguin Books, London, 1977

Barasch, Marc Ian, *The Healing Path*, Penguin Books (Arkana), London, 1995

Barbellion, W. N. P., *The Journal of a Disappointed Man*, Penguin Books in association with Chatto & Windus, London, 1948

Barnes, Julian, *Talking It Over*, Jonathan Cape, London, 1991

Bashford, Sir Henry Howard, *The Corner of Harley Street*, 1692

Beckett, Samuel, *Murphy*, Grove Press, New York, 1957

Beddoes, Thomas, *Death's Jest*, IV, 1850

Bell, Sir Charles, *The Hand*, 1824

Bell, Rudolph M., *Holy Anorexia*, University of Chicago Press, Chicago, 1985

Bennet, Glin, *The Wound And The Doctor*, Secker & Warburg, London, 1987
> *Patients and Their Doctors: The Journey through Medical Care*, Baillière Tindall, London, 1979

Bensley, Connie, *Central Reservations*, Bloodaxe Publications, Newcastle upon Tyne, 1990

Berger, John, and Mohr, Jean, *A Fortunate Man*, Granta, London, 1967

Bernard, Claude, *An Introduction to the Study of Experimental Medicine*, trans. Henry Copley Creene, Macmillan, New York, 1927

Berry, Wendell, *Openings*, Harcourt Brace and Co., San Diego, 1968

Betjeman, John, *Collected Poems*, John Murray, London, 1958

Biasin, Gian-Paolo, *Literary Diseases: Theme and Metaphor in the Italian Novel*, University of Texas Press, Austin and London, 1975

Billings, John Shaw, *Description of Johns Hopkins Hospital*, Baltimore, 1890

Black, Claudia, *It Will Never Happen to Me*, Mac Publications, Denver, Colorado, 1981

Blackmore, Sir Richard, *Creation*, VI, 1712

Blake, William, *Proverbs of Hell*, 1793
> *Songs of Experience*, 1794
> *Auguries of Innocence*, 1803
> *Jerusalem*, 1804
> *The Complete Poems*, ed. Alicia Ostriker, Penguin Books, London, 1977

Bly, Robert, *Iron John*, Element Books, London, 1991

Bovey, Shelley, *The Forbidden Body: Why Being Fat is Not a Sin*, Pandora, London, 1991

Bradstreet, Anne, *The Poems of Anne Bradstreet*, Dover Publications, New York, 1969

Brayfield, Celia, *Bestseller*, Fourth Estate, London, 1996

Brice, Judith Alexander, 'Empathy Lost', *Harvard Medical Alumni Bulletin*, 1987, 60 (4)

Brickhill, Paul, *Reach for the Sky*, Collins, London, 1957

Brontë, Emily, in *Poems by Currer, Ellis, and Acton Bell*, 1846

Brown, Christy, *The Childhood Story of Christy Brown* (previously entitled *My Left Foot*), Pan Books, London, 1972

Brown, Glynn, *Independent*, 29 January 1997

Brown, John, *Horae Subsecivae*, 3 vols., 1858–82

Browne, William, *Britannia's Pastorals*, 1616

Browning, Elizabeth Barrett, *Aurora Leigh*, 1856

Browning, Robert, *The Poems*, Vol. 1, ed. John Pettigrew, Penguin Books, London, 1981

Burnett, Frances Hodgson, *The Secret Garden*, Penguin Books (Puffin), London, 1967

Burns, Robert, *Selected Poems* ed. Carol McGuirt, Penguin Books, London, 1993

Burton, Robert, *The Anatomy of Melancholy*, 1621

Butler, Samuel, *Erewhon*, 1872

Butler, Sandra, *Conspiracy of Silence: The Trauma Of Incest*, Volcano Press, San Francisco, 1978

Byron, Lord, *Don Juan*, 1819–24

Caldwell, Taylor, *Dear and Glorious Physician*, Collins, London, 1959

Cameron, Julia, *The Artist's Way*, Pan, London, 1995

Campion, Thomas, *Works*, ed. P. Vivian, 1909

Camus, Albert, *Selected Essays and Notebooks*, trans. Philip Thody, Penguin Books, London, 1970
> *The Plague*, trans. Stuart Gilbert, Penguin Books, London, 1960

Capra, Fritjof, *The Turning Point: Science, Society and the Rising Culture*, Flamingo, London, 1983

Carlson, Richard and Shield, Benjamin, eds., *Healers on Healing*, Rider, London, 1990

Carlyle, Thomas, *Letters of Thomas Carlyle*, ed. C. E. Norton, 1888

Carmichael, Alexander (collected and translated by) *The Sun Dances: Prayers and Blessings from the Gaelic*, Floris Books, Edinburgh, 1988

Carroll, Lewis, *Through the Looking Glass*, 1871

Chekhov, Anton, *Selected Stories*, trans. Ann Dunigan, New American Library, New York, 1960
> *Anton Chekhov's Plays*, trans. and ed. Eugene K. Bristow, Norton, New York, 1977 (*The Three Sisters*)
> *The Duel and Other Stories*, trans. Ronald Wilks, Penguin Books, London, 1984

Churchill, Charles, *The Epistle to William Hogarth*, 1763
> *Gotham*, 1764

Clare, John, *Selected Poems*, Dent, London, 1970

Clarke, Lindsay, *Alice's Masque*, Jonathan Cape, London, 1994

Clendening, Logan, ed., *Source Book of Medical History*, Dover Publications, 1960

Clough, Arthur Hugh, 'The Latest Decalogue', 1849
> *Dipsychus*, 1865
> *Life is Struggle*, 1865

Clowes, William, *Profitable and Necessary Book of Observations*, 1596

Coelho, Paulo, *By the River Piedra I Sat Down and Wept*, HarperCollins, London, 1996

Coleridge, S. T., *Dejection: An Ode*, 1802
    Notebooks, 1895
    Poetical Works, OUP, London, 1969
Collop, John, *Itur Sic Satyricum*, 1660
Connolly, Cyril (Palinurus), *The Unquiet Grave*, Hamish Hamilton, London, 1973
Cowley, Abraham, *The Cure*, 1647
    Poems, 1656
Cowper, William, *Olney Hymns* (with John Newton), 1779
    The Task, 1785
    The Shrubbery, 1791
    Selected Poems of Thomas Gray, Charles Churchill and William Cowper, ed. Katherine Turner, Penguin Books, London, 1997
Crabbe, George, *The Borough*, 1810
Cronin, A. J., *The Stars Look Down*, Gollancz, London, 1937
cummings, e. e., *Complete Poems 1904–1962*, ed. George J. Firmage, Norton, New York, 1991
Da Costa, John Chalmers, *The Trials and Triumphs of the Surgeon*, Dorrance and Co., Philadelphia, 1944
Dale, Peter, *Mortal Fire*, Agenda Editions, 1976
Darwin, Erasmus, *The Botanic Garden*, 1789
    Zoonomia, 1795
Davies, Robertson, *The Papers of Samuel Marchbanks*, Viking, New York, 1986
Dearden, Harold, *Time and chance*, Heinemann, London, 1940
Dickens, Charles, *Oliver Twist*, 1838
    Nicholas Nickleby, 1839
    The Old Curiosity Shop, 1840
    Martin Chuzzlewit, 1844
    Hard Times, 1854
    Little Dorrit, 1857
    American Notes, 1860
Dickey, James, *The Eye Beaters*, Hamish Hamilton, London, 1971
Dickinson, Emily, *The Complete Poems of Emily Dickinson*, The Belknap Press of Harvard University Press, Cambridge, Mass., 1983
Donleavy, J. P., *The Ginger Man*, Penguin Books, London, 1968
Donne, John, *Devotions upon Emergent Occasions*, ed. Anthony Raspa, OUP, 1987
    Devotions upon Emergent Occasions: Selected Prose, chosen by Evelyn Simpson, OUP, 1967
    Complete English Poems, ed. A. J. Smith, Penguin Books, London, 1971

Dostoevsky, Feodor, *Notes from Underground*, 1864

Douglas, Christopher Home, *Searches for Summer*, 1874

Downie, R. S., *The Healing Arts: An Oxford Illustrated Anthology*, OUP, 1995

Dryden, John, *Epistles*, 1700
    Fables Ancient and Modern, 1700

Duff, Kat, *The Alchemy of Illness*, Virago Press, London, 1994

Duffey, Mary, *Missing Pieces: A Chronicle of Living with Disability*, Temple UP, Philadelphia, 1982

Dumas, Alexandre, *Proverbs 17:22*, 1863

Dunbar, William, *The Poems of William Dunbar*, Clarendon Press, Oxford, 1979

Dyer, Louis, *The Gods In Greece*, 1891

Dylan, Bob, 'Chimes of Freedom', Warner Bros. Inc., 1964
    'To Ramona', Warner Bros. Music, 1964a
    'Highway 61 Revisited', Warner Bros. Inc., 1965
    'Forever Young', Ram's Horn Music, 1973, 1974
    'Idiot Wind', Ram's Horn Music, 1974, 1975
    'Shelter from the Storm', Ram's Horn Music, 1974, 1975a
    'Where are You Tonight?', Special Rider Music, 1978
    'Every Grain of Sand', Special Rider Music, 1981
    'Shot of Love', Special Rider Music, 1981a
    'Don't Fall apart on Me Tonight', Special Rider Music, 1983
    'Jokerman', Special Rider Music, 1983a

Dyson, James, *Natural Medicines Society Newsletter*, No. 17, May 1991, Derby

Edelstein and Edelstein, *Asclepius: Testimonies*, Johns Hopkins Press, Baltimore, 1945

Eisenberg, Leon, 'The Physician As Interpreter', *Comprehensive Psychiatry* 22

Eliade, Mircea, *Shamanism: Archaic Techniques of Ecstasy*, trans. W. R. Trask, Arkana, London, 1989

Eliot, George, 'Janet's Repentance' in *Scenes of Clerical Life*, 1857
    Adam Bede, 1859
    Middlemarch, 1872

Eliot, T. S., *Four Quartets*, Faber, London, 1944
    The Cocktail Party, Faber, London, 1949

Ellis, Normandi, *Awakening Osiris*, Phanes Press, Michigan, 1988

Epic of Gilgamesh, ed. N. K. Sanders, Penguin Books, London, 1972

Estes, Clarissa Pinkola, *Women Who Run with the Wolves*, Rider, New York, 1992

Ezekiel, Nissim, *Latter Day Psalms*, OUP, India, 1982

Fanthorpe, U. A., *Selected Poems*, Penguin Books, London, 1986

Fine, Carla, *Married to Medicine: An Intimate Portrait of Doctors' Wives*, Atheneum, New York, 1981

Flatman, Thomas, *Poems and Songs*, 1674

Fortune, Dion, *Moon Magic*, Aquarian Press, Northampton, 1989

Frank, Arthur, *At the Will of the Body*, Houghton Mifflin Co., Boston, 1991

Frank, J., 'Nuclear Death – The Challenge of Ethical Religion', *The Ethical Platform*, 29 April 1962

Freud, Sigmund, *The Future of an Illusion*, Hogarth Press, London, 1962

Friedberger, Julie, *A Visible Wound: A Healing Journey through Breast Cancer*, Element, Dorset, 1996

Furlong, Monica, *Wise Child*, Gollancz, London, 1987

The Musician's World, trans. Daphne Woodward and others, ed. Hans Gal, Thames & Hudson, London, 1985

Garth, Sir Samuel, *The Dispensary*, 1699

Gaskell, Elizabeth, *Ruth*, 1853

Gay, John, *Fables*, 1727

Gibran, Kahlil, *The Prophet*, Heinemann, London, 1926
    The Wanderer, Knopf, New York, 1932

Gilbert, W. S., *Iolanthe*, 1882

Gillies, Margaret, *Give Me the Hill-Run Boys*, Outposts Publications, Walton-on-Thames, 1978

Girtin, Thomas, *The House I Live In*, 1872

Goethe, F. W. von, 'The Holy Longing', 1814

Goldsmith, Oliver, *The Captivity: An Oratorio*, 1801

Gordon, Richard, *The Literary Companion to Medicine*, Sinclair-Stevenson, London, 1993

Grant, Linda, 'Mother We Hardly Knew You', *Guardian*, 22 April 1996

Grass, Günter, *Local Anaesthetic*, trans. Ralph Manheim, Secker & Warburg, London, 1970

Graves, Robert, *On English Poetry*, Heinemann, London, 1922

Gray, Thomas, *The Poetical Works of Thomas Gray*, 1787

Brothers Grimm, *Grimms' Fairy Tales*, Penguin Books, London, 1995

Groddeck, Georg, *The Book of the It*, Vision Press, London, 1979

Gunn, Thom, *Selected Poems*, Faber, London, 1979

Haldane, J. B. S., *Everything Has a History*, Allen & Unwin, London, 1951
    Cancer's a Funny Thing, 1964

Hamilton, Mary, *Incubation*, Henderson & Son, St Andrews, 1906

Hardy, Thomas, *Collected Poems of Thomas Hardy*, Macmillan, London, 1960

Hartmann, Franz, *The Life and Prophecies of Paracelsus*, Rudolf Steiner Publications, New York, 1973

Hauschka, Dr Margarethe, *Health and the Human Spirit*, Elidyr Press, 1984

Hawthorne, Nathaniel, *The Haunted Mind*, 1839
 The Scarlet Letter, 1850

Hay, Louise, *Heal Your Body*, Eden Grove, London, 1984

Heine, Heinrich, *Poetical Works*, trans. Peter Branscombe, Penguin Books, London, 1967

Heller, Erick, *The Artist's Journey into the Interior*, Secker & Warburg, London, 1966

Hemingway, Ernest, *A Farewell to Arms*, Jonathan Cape, London, 1929

Henley, W. E., in *In Hospital*, Katabasis, London, 1992

Herbert, Cicely, in *In Hospital*, Katabasis, London, 1992

Herbert, George, *The Temple*, 1633

Herman, Judith L., 'Foreword' to Sandra Butler, *Conspiracy of Silence*, Volcano Press, San Francisco, 1978

Herrick, Robert, *Hesperides*, 1648

Hillman, James, *Suicide and the Soul*, Hodder & Stoughton, London, 1964
 Re-visioning Psychology, Harper & Row, New York, 1975
 Interviews, Harper & Row, New York, 1983
 The Soul's Code, Random House, New York, 1996
 Pan and the Nightmare, Spring Publications, Dallas, 1998

Hippocrates, *Hippocratic Writings*, ed. G. E. R. Lloyd, Penguin Books, London, 1978

Holmes, Oliver Wendell, *The Autocrat of the Breakfast Table*, 1858
 Currents and Counter-Currents in Medical Science, 1866
 Over the Teacups, 1891

Hood, Thomas, *Favourite Poems*, 1877

Hopkins, Anthony, *Films Illustrated*, December, 1980

Hopkins, Gerard Manley, *The Poems of Gerard Manley Hopkins*, OUP, Oxford, 1967

Horwood, William, *Skallagrigg*, Viking, London, 1987

Hull, John, *Touching the Rock: An Experience of Blindness*, Arrow, London, 1990

Hunt, Leigh, *Wit and Humour*, 1846

Huysmans, Joris-Karl, *Against Nature*, trans. Robert Baldick, Penguin Books, London, 1959

Ignatow, David, *Ignatow Poems 1934–1969*, Wesleyan University Press, Connecticut, 1970

Illich, Ivan, *Medical Nemesis*, Calder & Boyars, London, 1975

Irving, Washington, *The Sketch-Book of Geoffrey Crayon Gent*, 1819–20

Jerome, Jerome K., *Three Men in a Boat*, Penguin Books, London, 1995

Johnson, Samuel, *On the Death of Doctor Robert Levet*, 1783

Jonson, Ben, *An Anatomy of the World*, 1616
> *Letters*, ed. R. W. Chapman, Clarendon Press, Oxford, 1952

Joyce, James, *Portrait of the Artist as a Young Man*, Penguin Books, London, 1995

Jung, C. G., *The Spirit in Man, Art and Literature*, trans. R. F. C. Hull, Collected Works, Vol. 15, Routledge & Kegan Paul, London, 1966
> *The Practice of Psychotherapy*, trans. R. F. C. Hull, Collected Works, Vol. 16, Routledge & Kegan Paul, London, 1966a
> *Memories, Dreams, Reflections*, Fontana (Flamingo), London, 1987

Kafka, Franz, *Collected Stories*, ed. N. N. Glatzer, Penguin Books, London, 1992

Kalweit, Holger, *Shamans, Healers and Medicine Men*, Shambala, Boston, 1992

Keats, John, *The Fall of Hyperion*, 1819
> *Letters*, ed. H. E. Rollins, Harvard UP, Boston, 1958
> *John Keats' Poems*, Dent (Everyman), London, 1969

Keller, Helen, *The Story of My Life*, Hodder & Stoughton, London, 1951

King, Francis, *Questions of Life, Death and Hospital Visitors*, *Independent*, London, 5 December 1988

Kipling, Rudyard, *Barrack Room Ballads*, 1892
> *Just So Stories*, 1902

Kleinman, Arthur, *The Illness Narratives*, Basic Books, New York, 1988

Kramer, Larry, *The Normal Heart*, Nick Hern, London, 1993

Kubler-Ross, Elizabeth, *On Death and Dying*, Tavistock Publications, London, 1979

La Bruyère, *Les caractères*, 1688

Laing, R. D., *The Divided Self*, Penguin Books (Pelican), London, 1965

Lamb, Charles, *Complete Works of Charles Lamb*, Chatto & Windus, London, 1898

Lawrence, D. H., *Letters*, vol. 6, ed. J. T. Boulton, CUP, 1991
> *Apocalypse*, Penguin Books, London, 1995
> *Complete Poems*, Penguin Books, London, 1996

Leacock, Stephen, *Moonbeams from the Larger Lunacy*, Sutton, Gloucester, 1984
> *Literary Lapses*, Penguin Books, London, 1939

Lee, Laurie, *Cider with Rosie*, Penguin Books, London, 1962

Lewis, C. S., *The Problem of Pain*, Collins (Fontana), London, 1976.

Lewis, C. S., *A Grief Observed*, Faber, London, 1961

Lloyd Davies, M. and T. A., *The Bible: Medicine and Myth*, Silent Books, Cambridge, 1993

Lockheart, Russell, *Cancer in Myth and Dream*, Spring Publications, Connecticut, 1977

Lowbury, Edward, *Selected and New Poems*, Hippopotamus Press, Somerset, 1990
> *Daylight Astronomy: The Phoenix Living Poets*, Chatto & Windus with the Hogarth Press, London, 1968
> *Miracle Cure: The Nightwatchman*, Chatto & Windus, London, 1968a

Lucretius, *Concerning the Nature of Things*, trans. John Mason Good, London, 1805

Lyly, John, *Endimion*, 1588

Lynch, Thomas, *The Undertaking*, Jonathan Cape, London, 1997

MacCallum, John Bruce, *Short Years*, Normandie House, Chicago, 1938

McEwan, Ian, *The Innocent*, Jonathan Cape, London, 1990

Macey, Joanna, *Despair and Personal Power in the Nuclear Age*, New Society, Philadelphia, 1983

Maimonides, *The Guide of the Perplexed*, Shlomo Press, Chicago, 1963

Mann, Thomas, *Dr Faustus*, trans. H. T. Lowe-Porter, Dent, London, 1992
> *The Magic Mountain*, trans. H. T. Lowe-Porter, Minerva, London, 1996

Marquis, Don, *The Best of Don Marquis*, Doubleday, New York, 1946

Marvell, Andrew, *A Dialogue between the Soul and the Body*, 1681

Matthews, Caitlin, ed., *The Little Book of Celtic Blessings*, Element Books, Dorset, 1993

Maugham, W. Somerset, *Points of View*, New York, Doubleday, 1959
> *Of Human Bondage*, 1915

May, Rollo, *Love And Will*, W. W. Norton, New York, 1969
> *My Quest for Beauty*, Saybrook, Dallas, 1985

Meade, Michael, *Men and the Water of Life*, Harper, San Francisco, 1993

Menage, Gilles, *Menagiana*, 1650

Mérimée, Prosper, *Lettres à une inconnue*, 1874

Mereau-Ponty, Maurice, *The Phenomenology of Perception*, trans. C. Smith, Humanities Press, New Jersey, 1962

Meynell, Alice, *Poems*, Burns, Oates & Washbourne, London, 1913

Mill, J. S., *Autobiography*, Columbia University Press, Columbia, 1873

Miller, Jonathan, *The Body in Question*, Jonathan Cape, London, 1978

Milnes, Richard Monckton, *Poetical Works*, 1876

Milton, John, *Paradise Lost*, XI, 1667
> *Samson Agonistes*, 1671

Montaigne, Michel de, *The Essays of Michel de Montaigne*, trans. M. A. Screech, Penguin Books, London, 1991
    Essays, trans. J. M. Cohen, Penguin Books, London, 1958
Moore, Thomas, *Poetical Works*, 1801
Moore, Thomas, *Care of the Soul: How to Add Depth and Meaning to Your Everyday Life*, Piatkus, London, 1992
Morris, David B., 'Beauty and Pain: Notes on the Art of Richard Selzer', *The Iowa Review*, Spring–Summer 1980, Vol. 11, Nos. 2–3
Moss, Richard, 'The Mystery of Wholeness', in *Healers on Healing*, ed. Richard Carlson and Benjamin Shield, J. P. Tarcher Inc., New York, 1989
Mott, Valentine, *Pain and Anaesthetics*, 1865
Mount, Ferdinand, *Of Love and Asthma*, Mandarin, London, 1992
Muggeridge, Malcolm, *New Statesman*, 3 August 1962
Muller, Herbert J., *Science and Criticism*, Yale University Press, New Haven, 1943
Munthe, Axel, *The Story of San Michele*, John Murray, London, 1949
Murphy, Robert, *The Body Silent*, Phoenix House, London, 1987
Needleman, Jacob, *The Way of the Physician*, Penguin Books (Arkana), London, 1992
Nietzsche, Friedrich, *The Gay Science*, trans. W. Kaufman, Vintage, New York, 1974
    Beyond Good and Evil, trans. R. J. Hollingdale, Penguin Books, London, 1973
    Twilight of the Idols/The Antichrist, trans. R. J. Hollingdale, Penguin Books, London, 1968
Nightingale, Florence, *Notes on Nursing*, 1860
Norwood, Robin, *Why Me, Why This, Why Now?*, Arrow, London, 1995
Nouwen, Henri, *The Wounded Healer*, Doubleday, New York, 1972
Noyes, Alfred, *Collected Poems*, John Murray, London, 1950
Oliver, Mary, *Dreamwork*, Atlantic Monthly Press, 1986
Osler, Sir William, *Aequanimitas*, H. K. Lewis, London, 1904
Ovid, *Metamorphoses*, trans. Rolfe Humphries, Penguin Books, London, 1995
Owen, Goronwy, *Poetical Works*, 1876
Owen, Wilfred, *Collected Poems of Wilfred Owen*, Chatto & Windus, London, 1963
Page, Christine R., *Frontiers of Health*, C. W. Daniel, Essex, 1992
Paget, Stephen, *Confessio Medici*, Macmillan, London, 1908
Palinurus (Cyril Connolly), *The Unquiet Grave*, Hamish Hamilton, London, 1973

Paracelsus, *Selected Writings*, ed. Jolande Jacobi, Princeton University Press, Princeton, 1951.

Parris, Samuel Bartlett, *The Remains of Samuel Bartlett Parris*, ed. J. D., Plymouth, Mass., 1829
Anticipations and Recollections

Pasternak, Boris, *Dr Zhivago*, trans. Hayward and Harari, HarperCollins, London, 1995

Patch, Blanche, *Thirty Years with G.B.S.*, Gollancz, London, 1951

Peck, M. Scott, *A World Waiting to be Born*, Rider, London, 1993

Perls, Fritz, *The Gestalt Approach and Eyewitness to Therapy*, Bantam, New York, 1976

Pessoa, Fernando, *The Book of Disquiet*, ed. Maria Jose de Lancastre, trans. Margaret Jull Costa, Serpent's Tail, London, 1991

Pirani, Alex, 'Energy and Character', *Asthma*, IX, 3, 1978

Plath, Sylvia, *Selected Poems*, ed. Ted Hughes, Faber, London, 1985

Plato, *Symposium*, trans. Walter Hamilton, Penguin Books, London, 1951
    The Timaeus, trans. H. D. P. Lee, Penguin Books, London, 1965

Pliny the Elder, *Natural History*, trans. John F. Healey, Penguin Books, London, 1991

Pope, Alexander, *Works*, 1751

Powys, John Cowper, *A Glastonbury Romance*, MacDonald, London, 1933

Prior, Matthew, *Alma, or The Progress of the Mind* (Canto I), 1718

Proust, Marcel, *The Remembrance of Things Past*, Penguin Books, London, 1995

Raine, Kathleen, *The Pythoness and Other Poems*, Hamish Hamilton, London, 1949
    Selected Poems, Golgonooza Press, Ipswich, 1988

Ransford, Tessa, *Fools and Angels*, The Ramsay Head Press, Edinburgh, 1984

Reade, W. Winwood, *The Martyrdom of Man*, 1872

Reiser, David, and Rosen, David, *Medicine as a Human Experience*, University Park Press, Baltimore, 1984

Remen, Rachel Naomi, *Kitchen Table Wisdom*, Pan, London, 1997

Rhodes, Enid, ed., *Medicine and Literature*, Neale Watson, 1980 ('Peschel')

Rilke, Rainer Maria, *Letters to a Young Poet*, W. W. Norton, New York, 1954
    Rilke on Love and other Difficulties, trans. J. J. L. Mood, W. W. Norton, New York, 1975

Robinson, Victor, *The Story of Medicine*, Tudor Publishing Co., New York, 1931

Roethke, Theodore, *Collected Poems*, Faber, London, 1986

Ross, Sir Ronald, *Success in Malaria Research*, 1897

Rous, Francis, *Oile of Scorpions*, 1623

Rousseau, J.-J., *Émile*, 1762

Rumi, *Poems of Rumi*, trans. and spoken by Robert Bly and Coleman Barks, Audioliterature, Berkeley, CA (sound recording)

Sacks, Oliver, *A Leg to Stand On*, Picador, London, 1989
  Awakenings, Picador, London, 1973

Sandburg, Carl, *Corn Huskers*, 1918

Sanford, John A., *Healing and Wholeness*, Paulist Press, New York, 1977

Santayana, George *The Life of Reason*, Constable/MIT Press, 1905

Sardello, Robert, *Facing the World with Soul*, Lindisfarne Press, New York, 1992

Sassoon, Siegfried, *Collected Poems 1908–56*, Faber, London, 1961

Schenk, Ronald, in *The Body in Analysis*, ed. Nathan Schwartz-Salant and Murray Stein, Chiron, Illinois, 1986

Schmookler, Andrew Bard, *The Parable of Tribes*, University of California Press, Berkeley, 1984

Schweitzer, Albert, *Out of My Life and Thought: An Autobiography*, trans. C. T. Campion, Henry Holt, New York, 1933
  Memoirs of Childhood and Youth, trans. C. T. Campion, Macmillan, New York, 1949

Sergeant, Howard, ed., *Poems from the Medical World*, MTP Press, Lancaster, 1979

Selzer, Richard, *Rituals of Surgery*, Touchstone, New York, 1974
  'Mercy', *The Iowa Review*, Spring–Summer 1980, Vol. 11, Nos. 2–3
  in *Healing Arts in Dialogue: Medicine and Literature*, ed. Joanne Trautmann, Southern Illinois University Press, 1981a
    Confessions of a Knife, Paladin, London, 1982
    Mortal Lessons, Simon & Schuster, New York, 1977

Seneca, *Dialogues and Letters*, ed. C. D. N. Costa, Penguin Books, 1997

Sexton, Anne, *Live or Die*, OUP, 1967

Shaw, George Bernard, *Back to Methuselah*, 1921
  The Doctor's Dilemma, Penguin Books, London, 1948

Shelley, P. B., Queen Mab, 1813
  Shelley's Poetry and Prose, W. W. Norton, New York, 1977

Shin, Nan, *Diary of a Zen Nun: Every Day Living*, E. P. Dutton, London, 1986

Shore, Henry, *Selected Poems*, Outposts Publications, Walton-on-Thames, 1976

Siegel, Bernie S., *Love, Medicine and Miracles*, Harper & Row, 1986

Peace, Love and Healing: The Path To Self-Healing, Arrow Books, New York, 1993

Sigerist, Henry E., *The Great Doctors*, Allen & Unwin, London, 1933
> *A History of Medicine*, OUP, Oxford, 1951

Silverstein, Shel, *Where the Sidewalk Ends: The Poems and Drawings of Shel Silverstein*, Jonathan Cape, London, 1984

Smart, Christopher, *Hymn to the Supreme Being on Recovery from a Dangerous Fit of Illness*, 1756

Smith, Stevie, *Collected Poems of Stevie Smith*, Penguin Books, London, 1985

Smollett, Tobias, *The Adventures of Peregrine Pickle*, 1751

Solle, Dorothee, *Suffering*, Fortress Press, 1975

Solzhenitsyn, Alexander, *Cancer Ward*, The Bodley Head, London, 1968

Some, Malidoma Patrice, *Ritual: Power, Healing and Community*, Swan Raven & Co., Portland, 1993
> *Of Water and the Spirit: Ritual, Magic and Initiation in the Life of an African Shaman*, Penguin Books (Arkana), London, 1995

Sontag, Susan, *Illness as Metaphor*, Penguin Books, London, 1978

Starhawk, *Truth or Dare*, Harper & Row, New York, 1987

Steiner, Rudolf, *Lucifer and Ahriman*, Steiner Book Centre, N. Vancouver, 1976
> *Health and Illness*, Anthroposophic Press, Spring Valley, New York, 1981

Stekel, Wilhelm, *Conditions of Nervous Anxiety and Their Treatment*, trans. Rosalie Gabler, Routledge & Kegan Paul, London, 1923

Stephen, Julia Duckworth, *Stories for Children and Adults*, ed. Diane F. Gillespie, Elizabeth Steele, 1987

Sterne, Laurence, *Collected Works*, 1780

Stevenson, Robert Louis, *An Inland Voyage*, 1877
> *Virginibus Puerisque*, 1881
> *A Child's Garden of Verses*, 1885
> *Crabbed Age and Youth*, 1885a
> *Underwoods*, 1887
> *Ordered South*, 1891

Swift, Jonathan, *Jonathan Swift: Letters*, ed. Harold Williams, Clarendon Press, Oxford, 1963
> *The Complete Poems*, ed. Pat Rogers, Penguin Books, London, 1983

Sydney, Sir Philip, *Poetical Works*, 1873

Tennyson, Alfred Lord, *In Memoriam* (Canto CVI), 1850

Mother Teresa, *Daily Readings*, ed. Teresa de Bertodano, Fount, 1993

Thomas, Gospel of, in J. M. Robinson, *The Nag Hammadi Library*, Harper & Row, New York, 1977

Thomas, D. M., *Selected Poems*, Secker & Warburg, London, 1983

Thomas, Jill, in *Poems from the Medical World*, ed. Howard Sergeant, MTP Press, 1979

Thomas, Lewis, *The Medusa and the Snail*, Allen Lane, London, 1980
    The Youngest Science, Viking Press, New York, 1983
    The Youngest Science, OUP, Oxford, 1985
    The Fragile Species, Charles Scribner's Sons, New York, 1992

Thomas, R. S., *Collected Poems*, Dent, London, 1993

Thompson, William Irwin, *The Time Falling Bodies Take to Light*, Rider/ Hutchinson, New York, 1981

Thoreau, Henry, *Journal*, Princeton University Press, 1906

Tolstoy, Leo, *War and Peace*, trans. L. and A. Maude, Macmillan, London, 1960
    The Death of Ivan Ilyich and Other Stories, trans. with an introduction by Rosemary Edmonds, Penguin Books, London, 1960

Toolis, Kevin, 'A Death in the Family', *The Guardian Weekend*, 6 July 1996

Treves, Sir Frederick, *Two Women*, 1883

Turgenev, Ivan, *Selected Stories of Ivan Turgenev*, trans. Constance Garnett, Heinemann, London, 1974

Twain, Mark, *The Mysterious Stranger*, published in serial form, 1916

Unamuno, Miguel de, *Selected Works*, ed. Anthony Kerrigan, Routledge & Kegan Paul, London, 1967

Updike, John, *Self-Consciousness: Memoirs*, André Deutsch, London, 1989

Valéry, Paul, *Monsieur Teste*, trans. Jackson Mathews, Routledge & Kegan Paul, London, 1973

van der Post, Sir Laurens, *The Heart of the Hunter*, Penguin Books, London, 1965
    The Lost World of the Kalahari, Penguin Books, London, 1962
    A Story Like the Wind, Chatto & Windus, London, 1985
    Venture to the Interior, Hogarth Press, London, 1952

van Dyke, Henry, *The Story of the Other Wise Man*, Harper & Brothers, New York, 1905

Vaughan, Henry, *Collected Works*, 1871

Vine, Barbara, *King Soloman's Carpet*, Viking, London, 1991

Walker, Alice, *Living by the Word: Selected Writings 1973–87*, The Women's Press, London, 1988
    The Temple of My Familiar, Penguin Books, London, 1990

Ward, Ann, *A Music Lesson (A Therapy Class for Brain-Damaged Children)*, Outposts Publications, Walton-on-Thames, 1974

Watts, Alan W., *Myth and Ritual in Christianity*, Beacon Press, Boston, 1968

Watts, Isaac, *Hymns and Spiritual Songs*, 1719

Weil, Simone, *Waiting for God*, trans. Craufurd, Routledge & Kegan Paul, London, 1979

Weinman Lear, Martha, *Heartsounds*, Simon & Schuster, New York, 1980

White, E. B., *Writings from the New Yorker 1927–1976*, Harper Perennial, New York, 1990

Whitman, Walt, *Leaves of Grass*, fifth edition, 1871
    Drum Taps, 1865

Whittier, John Greenleaf, *To a Young Physician*, 1889

Whone, Herbert, *Church Monastery Cathedral*, Element Books, Dorset, 1990

Wilcox, Ella Wheeler, *Collected Poems*, London, 1921

Wilde, Oscar, *The Importance of Being Earnest*, 1895
    Letters, ed. R. Hart-Davis, Hart-Davis, London, 1962

Williams, Roger, *Nutrition against Disease*, Pitman Publishing Company, New York, 1971

Williams, William Carlos, *Collected Poems*, ed. C. MacGowan, Paladin, St Albans, 1951
    Autobiography, New Directions, New York, 1967
    The Doctor Stories, ed. Robert Coles, Faber, London, 1984

Wilson, A. N., *The Healing Art*, Reed Consumer Books, London, 1982

Winterson, Jeannette, *Art and Lies*, Jonathan Cape, London, 1995

Wolcot, John, *Expostulatory Odes*, 1789

Wood, Nancy, *Hollering Sun*, Simon & Schuster, New York, 1972

Woolf, Virginia, *The Moment and Other Essays*, Hogarth Press, London, 1967

Wordsworth, William, *The Tables Turned*, 1802
    Preface to *The Lyrical Ballads*, 1802
    Wordsworth: Poetical Works, OUP, Oxford, 1969

Yalom, Irvin D., *Existential Psychotherapy*, New York, Basic Books, 1980

Young, Edward, *The Complaint, or Night Thoughts on Life, Death and Immortality*, 1742–4

Zinsser, Hans, *As I Remember Him*, Macmillan, London, 1940

Acknowledgements

The editor and publishers gratefully acknowledge permission to reprint the following copyright material in this book:

DANNIE ABSE: extracts from 'The Stethoscope', 'In Llandough Hospital', 'X-Ray', 'The Doctor' and 'Pantomime Diseases' from *White Coat, Purple Coat: Collected Poems 1948–1988* (Hutchinson, 1989), reprinted by permission of The Peters Fraser & Dunlop Group Ltd; W. H. AUDEN: extract from 'Surgical Ward' from *Selected Poems*, The Penguin Poets, 1967, reprinted by permission of Faber & Faber Ltd; WENDELL BERRY: 'The Peace of Wild Things' from *Openings*, © 1968 and renewed 1996 by Wendell Berry, reprinted by permission of Harcourt Brace & Company; JOHN BETJE-MAN: 'Five O'Clock Shadow' and an extract from 'A Child Ill' from *Collected Poems* (John Murray, 1958), reprinted by permission of the publishers; ANTON CHEKHOV: extracts from 'The Black Monk' from *The Duel and Other Stories*, translated by Ronald Wilks (Penguin Classics, 1984), © Ronald Wilks, 1984, reprinted by permission of Penguin Books Ltd; JOHN CLARE: extracts from 'Child Harold' and 'I Am' from *Selected Poems* (Dent, 1970), © Eric Robinson 1984, reprinted by permission of Curtis Brown Ltd, London; E. E. CUMMINGS: 'Progress is a comfortable disease' and 'a total stranger one black day' from *Complete Poems 1904–1962*, edited by George J. Firmage, © 1991 by the Trustees for the E. E. Cummings Trust and George James Firmage, reprinted by permission of W. W. Norton & Company; PETER DALE: an extract from 'Mortal Fire' from *Mortal Fire* (Agenda Editions, 1976), reprinted by permission of the author; EMILY DICKINSON: 'There is a pain so utter', 'My first well day – since many ill', 'If I can stop one heart from breaking', 'Surgeons must be very careful', 'They say that time assuages', 'A little madness in the spring', 'Much Madness is divinest Sense', 'New Periods – of Pain' and 'Because I could not stop for Death' from *The Poems of Emily Dickinson*, edited by Thomas H. Johnson

(Cambridge, Mass., The Belknap Press of Harvard University Press), © 1951, 1955, 1979, 1983 by the President and Fellows of Harvard College, reprinted by permission of the publishers and the Trustees of Amherst College; BOB DYLAN: lyrics from 'Idiot Wind', © 1974, 1975 by Ram's Horn Music, 'To Ramona', © 1964 by Warner Bros. Music, renewed 1993 by Special Rider Music, 'Where Are You Tonight?', © 1978 by Special Rider Music, 'Every Grain of Sand', © 1981 by Special Rider Music, 'Chimes of Freedom', © 1964 by Warner Bros. Inc., renewed 1992 by Special Rider Music, 'Highway 61 Revisited', © 1965 by Warner Bros. Inc., renewed 1993 by Special Rider Music, 'Shelter From the Storm', © 1974, 1975 by Ram's Horn Music, 'Don't Fall Apart on Me Tonight', © 1983 by Special Rider Music, 'Shot of Love', © 1981 by Special Rider Music, 'Jokerman', © 1983 by Special Rider Music, and 'Forever Young', © 1973, 1974 by Ram's Horn Music. All rights reserved. International copyright secured. Reprinted by permission of Special Rider Music; T. S. ELIOT: extracts from 'East Coker' from *Four Quartets*, from *Collected Poems 1909–1962* (Faber & Faber, 1974), reprinted by permission of the publishers; NISSIM EZEKIEL: 'Night of the Scorpion' from *Latter Day Psalms* (Oxford University Press India, 1982), reprinted by permission of the publishers; U. A. FANTHORPE: 'In-Patients' and 'After Visiting Hours' from *Selected Poems* (Penguin Books, 1986), reprinted by permission of the author; ARTHUR FRANK: extracts from *At the Will of the Body*, © 1991 by Arthur W. Frank and Catherine E. Foote, reprinted by permission of Houghton Mifflin Company. All rights reserved; an extract from *The Epic of Gilgamesh*, translated by N. K. Sandars (Penguin Classics, 1960; second revised edition, 1972), © N. K. Sandars, 1960, 1964, 1972, reprinted by permission of Penguin Books Ltd; MARGARET GILLIES: 'Turning Point', from *Poems from the Medical World*, edited by Howard Sergeant (MTP Press, 1979), reprinted by permission of Kluwer Academic Publishers; THOM GUNN: 'Baby Song' from *Selected Poems* (Faber & Faber, 1979), reprinted by permission of the publishers; WILLIAM HORWOOD: extracts from *Skallagrigg* (Viking, 1987), © Steppenmole Enterprises Ltd, 1987, reprinted by permission of Penguin Books Ltd; DAVID IGNATOW: 'Sunday at the State Hospital' from *Poems 1934–1969* (Wesleyan University Press, 1970), reprinted by permission of the author; ELIZABETH KUBLER-ROSS: extracts from *On Death and Dying* (Tavistock Publications, 1979), reprinted by permission of the publishers; D. H. LAWRENCE: extracts from *Apocalypse* (Penguin Books, 1995), extracts from *Complete Poems* (Penguin Books, 1996), and an extract from *Letters of D. H. Lawrence*, Volume 6, edited by J. T. Boulton (Cambridge University Press, 1991), reprinted by permission of Laurence Pollinger Limited and the Estate of Frieda Lawrence Ravagli; LAURIE LEE: extracts from *Cider with Rosie* (Penguin Books, 1962), reprinted by permission of Random House UK Ltd; an extract from *The Little Book of Celtic Blessings*, compiled by Caitlin Matthews (Element Books, 1993), reprinted by permission of the publishers; JONATHAN MILLER: extracts from *The Body in Question* (Jonathan Cape, 1978), reprinted by permission of David Higham Associates Ltd; NAOMI MITCH-ISON: 'Bowel Problems', reprinted by permission of David Higham Associates Ltd; FERDINAND MOUNT: extracts from *Of Love and Asthma* (Mandarin, 1992), reprinted by permission of Random House UK Ltd; AXEL MUNTHE: extracts from *The Story of San Michele* (John Murray, 1949), reprinted by permission of the publishers; ROBERT MURPHY: an extract from *The Body Silent* (Phoenix House, 1987), reprinted by permission of The Orion Publishing Group Ltd; ALFRED NOYES: an extract from 'The Remembering Garden' from *Collected Poems* (John Murray, 1950), reprinted by permission of Hugh Noyes; OVID: an extract from *Metamorphoses*, translated by Rolfe Humphries (Penguin Books, 1995), reprinted by permission of Indiana University Press; KATHLEEN RAINE: extracts from 'The Pythoness' and 'The Spell of Sleep', reprinted by permission of the author; TESSA RANSFORD: extracts from 'Hospitalisation' from *Fools and Angels* (Ramsay Head Press, 1984), reprinted by permission of the author; THEODORE ROETHKE: extracts from 'Infirmity', 'Meditation in Hydrotherapy', 'Lines on Leaving a Sanitorium', 'The Marrow' and 'In a Dark Time' from *The Collected Poems of Theodore Roethke* (Faber & Faber, 1986), reprinted by permission of the publishers; CARL SANDBURG: an extract from 'Wilderness' from *Corn Huskers* (1918), copyright 1918 by Holt, Rinehart & Winston, Inc., and renewed 1946 by Carl Sandburg, reprinted by permission of Harcourt Brace & Company; SIEGFRIED SAS-SOON: extracts from 'Counter-Attack' and 'The Death-Bed' from *Collected Poems 1908–1956* (Faber & Faber, 1961), reprinted by permission of George Sassoon; ANNE SEXTON: extracts from 'The Addict' and 'For the Year of the Insane' from *Live or Die* (Oxford University Press, 1967), reprinted by permission of The Peters Fraser & Dunlop Group Ltd; STEVIE SMITH: 'Not Waving but Drowning' and an extract from 'Away Melancholy' from *The Collected Poems of Stevie Smith* (Penguin Books, 1985), reprinted by permission of James MacGibbon; JILL THOMAS: 'Night Duty', reprinted in *Poems from the Medical World*, edited by Howard Sergeant (MTP Press, 1979), reprinted by permission of Kluwer Academic Publishers; LEWIS THOMAS: extracts from *The Fragile Species* (1992), © 1992 by Lewis Thomas, reprinted by permission of Scribner, a Division of Simon & Schuster; LEO TOLSTOY: extracts from *The Death of Ivan Ilyich and Other Stories*, translated by Rosemary Edmonds (Penguin Classics, 1960), © Rosemary Edmonds, 1960, reprinted by permission of Penguin Books Ltd; JOHN

UPDIKE: extracts from *Self Consciousness: memoirs* (Penguin Books, 1990), © John Updike, 1989, reprinted by permission of Penguin Books Ltd; ANN WARD: an extract from 'A Music Lesson', reprinted in *Poems from the Medical World*, edited by Howard Sergeant (MTP Press, 1979), reprinted by permission of Kluwer Academic Publishers; WILLIAM CARLOS WILLIAMS: 'The Last Words of My English Grandmother' and an extract from 'Asphodel' from *Collected Poems*, edited by C. J. MacGowan (Paladin, 1951), reprinted by permission of Carcanet Press Ltd; extracts from *The Doctor Stories* (Faber & Faber, 1984), reprinted by permission of Laurence Pollinger Ltd; VIRGINIA WOOLF: extracts from 'On Being Ill' from *The Moment and Other Essays* (The Hogarth Press, 1967), reprinted by permission of The Society of Authors as the Literary Representatives of the Estate of Virginia Woolf.

Every effort has been made to obtain permission from all copyright holders whose material is included in this book. Penguin would like to thank any copyright holders whose work is included without acknowledgement, and any omissions brought to the attention of the publishers will be rectified in future editions.

PENGUIN ONLINE

READ MORE IN PENGUIN

In every corner of the world, on every subject under the sun, Penguin represents quality and variety – the very best in publishing today.

For complete information about books available from Penguin – including Puffins, Penguin Classics and Arkana – and how to order them, write to us at the appropriate address below. Please note that for copyright reasons the selection of books varies from country to country.

In the United Kingdom: Please write to *Dept. EP, Penguin Books Ltd, Bath Road, Harmondsworth, West Drayton, Middlesex UB7 0DA*

In the United States: Please write to *Consumer Sales, Penguin Putnam Inc., P.O. Box 12289 Dept. B, Newark, New Jersey 07101-5289.* VISA and MasterCard holders call 1-800-788-6262 to order Penguin titles

In Canada: Please write to *Penguin Books Canada Ltd, 10 Alcorn Avenue, Suite 300, Toronto, Ontario M4V 3B2*

In Australia: Please write to *Penguin Books Australia Ltd, P.O. Box 257, Ringwood, Victoria 3134*

In New Zealand: Please write to *Penguin Books (NZ) Ltd, Private Bag 102902, North Shore Mail Centre, Auckland 10*

In India: Please write to *Penguin Books India Pvt Ltd, 11 Community Centre, Panchsheel Park, New Delhi 110017*

In the Netherlands: Please write to *Penguin Books Netherlands bv, Postbus 3507, NL-1001 AH Amsterdam*

In Germany: Please write to *Penguin Books Deutschland GmbH, Metzlerstrasse 26, 60594 Frankfurt am Main*

In Spain: Please write to *Penguin Books S. A., Bravo Murillo 19, 1° B, 28015 Madrid*

In Italy: Please write to *Penguin Italia s.r.l., Via Benedetto Croce 2, 20094 Corsico, Milano*

In France: Please write to *Penguin France, Le Carré Wilson, 62 rue Benjamin Baillaud, 31500 Toulouse*

In Japan: Please write to *Penguin Books Japan Ltd, Kaneko Building, 2-3-25 Koraku, Bunkyo-Ku, Tokyo 112*

In South Africa: Please write to *Penguin Books South Africa (Pty) Ltd, Private Bag X14, Parkview, 2122 Johannesburg*

READ MORE IN PENGUIN

A CHOICE OF NON-FICTION

Jane Austen: A Life Claire Tomalin

'I cannot think that a better life of Jane Austen than Claire Tomalin's will be written for many years . . . a truly marvellous book' *Mail on Sunday*. 'As near perfect a Life of Austen as we are likely to get . . . Tomalin presents Austen as remarkably clever; sensitive, but unsentimental' *Daily Telegraph*

A Wavering Grace Gavin Young

'By far . . . the most moving account of Vietnam to be written in recent years' Norman Lewis. 'This delicate, terrible and enchanting book . . . brings the atmosphere of Vietnam so near that you can almost taste and smell it' *The Times*

Clone Gina Kolata

On July 5 1996 Dolly, the most famous lamb in history, was born. It was an event of enormous significance, for Dolly was a clone, produced from the genetic material of a six-year-old ewe. Suddenly, the idea that human beings could be replicated had become a reality. 'Superb' J. G. Ballard, *Sunday Times*

Huxley Adrian Desmond

T. H. Huxley (1825–95), often referred to as 'Darwin's Bulldog', became the major champion of the theory of evolution and was crucial to the making of our modern Darwinian world. 'Nobody writes scientific biography like Adrian Desmond, and this account of Huxley's progress . . . is his best so far' *The Times Literary Supplement*

Cleared for Take-Off Dirk Bogarde

'It begins with his experiences in the Second World War as an interpreter of reconnaissance photographs . . . his awareness of the horrors as well as the dottiness of war is essential to the tone of this affecting and strangely beautiful book' *Daily Telegraph*

READ MORE IN PENGUIN

A CHOICE OF NON-FICTION

Time Out Film Guide   Edited by John Pym

The definitive, up-to-the-minute directory of every aspect of world cinema from classics and silent epics to reissues and the latest releases.

Four-Iron in the Soul   Lawrence Donegan

'A joy to read. Not since Bill Bryson plotted a random route through small-town America has such a breezy idea for a book had a happier (or funnier) result' *The Times*. 'Funny, beautifully observed and it tells you things about sport in general and golf in particular that nobody else thought to pass on' *Mail on Sunday*

Nelson Mandela: A Biography   Martin Meredith

Nelson Mandela's role in delivering South Africa from racial division stands as one of the great triumphs of the twentieth century. In this brilliant account, Martin Meredith gives a vivid portrayal of the life and times of this towering figure. 'The best biography so far of Nelson Mandela' Raymond Whitaker, *Independent on Sunday*

In Search of Nature   Edward O. Wilson

'*In Search of Nature* makes such stimulating reading that Edward O. Wilson might be regarded as a one-man recruitment bureau for tomorrow's biologists . . . His essays on ants tend to leave one gasping for breath, literally speaking . . . Yet he is equally enchanting in his accounts of sharks and snakes and New Guinea's birds of paradise' *The Times Higher Education Supplement*

Reflections on a Quiet Rebel   Cal McCrystal

This extraordinary book is both a vivid memoir of Cal McCrystal's Irish Catholic childhood and a loving portrait of his father Charles, a 'quiet rebel' and unique man. 'A haunting book, lovely and loving. It explains more about one blighted corner of Ireland than a dozen dogged histories' *Scotsman*

READ MORE IN PENGUIN

A CHOICE OF NON-FICTION

Falling Leaves   Adeline Yen Mah

'I am still haunted by Mah's memoir ... Riveting. A marvel of memory. Poignant proof of the human will to endure' Amy Tan. '*Falling Leaves* is a terrible and riveting family history ... It is also a story about endurance and the cost it can exact' *Daily Telegraph*

Anatomy of a Miracle   Patti Waldmeir

The peaceful birth of black majority rule in South Africa has been seen by many as a miracle – or at least political magic. 'Essential reading for anyone interested in South Africa' *Literary Review*. 'One of the most authoritative reporters on the South African scene ... her analytical skills are deadly' *Sunday Times*

My Name Escapes Me   Alec Guinness

'His diary for the eighteen months from January 1995 to June 1996 is a book of immense charm and the source of almost undiluted pleasure. Imagine a lucky dip where each entry comes up with a prize and you will have some measure of the writing' *Daily Mail*

The Feminization of Nature   Deborah Cadbury

Scientists around the world are uncovering alarming changes in human reproduction and health. There is strong evidence that sperm counts have fallen dramatically. Testicular and prostate cancer are on the increase. Different species are showing signs of 'feminization' or even 'changing sex'. 'Grips you from page one ... it reads like a Michael Crichton thriller' John Gribbin

The Portuguese   Marion Kaplan

This book records Portugal's rich and turbulent history and also ranges lightly across the issues, incongruities and paradoxes of Portugal today. 'Sympathetic, perceptive, lively and full of information' *The Times Literary Supplement*

READ MORE IN PENGUIN

A CHOICE OF NON-FICTION

Racers Richard Williams

'Where Williams really scores is in his evocation of the political chicanery and secret vendettas in Formula One' *Guardian*. 'Gets under the skin of this intelligent, sophisticated and cold-blooded sport ... the plot grips like Pirellis on a rain-slicked mountain pass' *Observer*

Floyd on Africa Keith Floyd

Keith Floyd's wonderful chronicle of cooking, eating and travelling around Zambia, Zimbabwe, Madagascar and South Africa is part safari and part recipe book. Inspired by the tropical fruits in the markets, the fish from sparkling lakes and the game from the bush, he conjures up some unforgettable meals.

The Way to Write John Fairfax and John Moat

While of direct use to the more practised writer, *The Way to Write* remains alive to the difficulties experienced by those who would like to explore their own creative writing but feel unsure of how to begin. This stimulating book takes you from the first confrontation with the blank page to the final manuscript.

The Little Book of Calm Paul Wilson

Feeling stressed? Need some help to regain balance in your life? The bestselling *The Little Book of Calm* is full of advice to follow and thoughts to inspire. Open it at any page and you will find a path to inner peace.

American Frontiers Gregory H. Nobles

'At last someone has written a narrative of America's frontier experience with sensitivity and insight. This is a book which will appeal to both the specialist and the novice' James M. McPherson, Princeton University

READ MORE IN PENGUIN

A CHOICE OF NON-FICTION

The Old Patagonian Express Paul Theroux

Beginning his journey in Boston, where he boarded the subway commuter train, Paul Theroux travelled the length of North and South America, to his destination in Patagonia. 'Fascinating, beautifully written ... a vivid travelogue described with the sensitive, richly observant pen of a born writer' *Sunday Express*

The Lions Diary Jeremy Guscott with Nick Cain

Packed with action from the pitch, the dressing-room and the heartlands, *The Lions Diary* is the complete insiders' account of the most successful tour in British rugby history. 'Hugely entertaining. If you want a book that tells it from the inside of a sweaty tracksuit after endless shuttle-runs, this is the one' *Daily Telegraph*

Michael Heseltine Michael Crick

'Michael Crick confirms his reputation as a superb investigator. He writes wittily and engagingly with a mastery of narrative pace as well as a shrewd political nose ... it should prove the definitive life' *The Times Literary Supplement*. 'Entertaining ... seems set to become the standard tome on his subject' *The Times*

Mornings in the Dark Edited by David Parkinson
The Graham Greene Film Reader

Prompted by 'a sense of fun' and 'that dangerous third Martini' at a party in June 1935, Graham Greene volunteered himself as the *Spectator* film critic. 'His film reviews are among the most trenchant, witty and memorable one is ever likely to read' *Sunday Times*

Fenland Chronicle Sybil Marshall

In *Fenland Chronicle* Sybil Marshall has collected together her mother's and father's remembrances of their childhood, marriage, family life and work in this traditional corner of England and drawn them into a vivid portrait of a time gone by.

READ MORE IN PENGUIN

A CHOICE OF NON-FICTION

The Penguin Opera Guide
Edited by Amanda Holden with Nicholas Kenyon and Stephen Walsh

'Remarkably comprehensive . . . The criterion for any guide is whether it can be read not only for reference but for entertainment, and Amanda Holden and her contributors pass this test with first-class honours' *The Times*

The 30-Minute Cook Nigel Slater

'An inspired worldwide collection of quick and accessible dishes; robust and honest, they are constructed so the ingredients shine, the cooking is simple, and the results impressive . . . Go shopping with a copy and feast on the pleasure of real food' *Evening Standard*

The Pleasures of the Past David Cannadine

'This is almost everything you ever wanted to know about the past but were too scared to ask . . . A fascinating book and one to strike up arguments in the pub' *Daily Mail*. 'He is erudite and rigorous, yet always fun. I can imagine no better introduction to historical study than this collection' *Observer*

Richard Feynman: A Life in Science John Gribbin and Mary Gribbin

'Richard Feynman (1918–88) was to the second half of the century what Einstein was to the first: the perfect example of scientific genius' *Independent*. 'One of the most influential and best-loved physicists of his generation . . . This biography is both compelling and highly readable' *Mail on Sunday*

A Sin Against the Future Vivien Stern

Do prisons contribute to a better, safer world? Or are they a threat to democracy, as increasingly punitive measures are brought in to deal with rising crime? This timely account examines different styles of incarceration around the world and presents a powerful case for radical change.

READ MORE IN PENGUIN

A CHOICE OF NON-FICTION

The Idea of India Sunil Khilnani

'Many books about India will be published this year; I doubt if any will be wiser and more illuminating about its modern condition than this' *Observer*. 'Sunil Khilnani's meditation on India since Independence is a *tour de force*' *Sunday Telegraph*

The Cretan Runner George Psychoundakis

The remarkable story of the shepherd boy who became a war-time runner for the Cretan Resistance. 'The book has at once the calm of a race which takes it for granted that life is full of death, and the excitement of a fighter who wildly enjoys his own part of the dangerous business. It is full of jokes and full of pride' *Sunday Times*

The Diary of a Young Girl Anne Frank

'Anne Frank's diary is one of the greatest books of the century . . . As she brings herself and her circumstances into such buzzing, engaged life on the page, she triumphs over her history. We return to her again and again, unable to believe that this hymn to life was written on the way to Belsen' *Guardian*

A History of Twentieth-Century Russia Robert Service

'A remarkable work of scholarship and synthesis . . . [it] demands to be read' *Spectator*. 'A fine book . . . It is a dizzying tale and Service tells it well; he has none of the ideological baggage that has so often bedevilled Western histories of Russia . . . A balanced, dispassionate and painstaking account' *Sunday Times*

Word from Wormingford Ronald Blythe

'This book is a little masterpiece. It comprises a collection of Blythe's writings about the parish year at his Suffolk village of Wormingford . . . his integrity, unwavering Christian faith, wisdom, sense of wonder and absolute love of nature and her seasonal rhythms blaze from every page' Val Hennessy, *Daily Mail*

READ MORE IN PENGUIN

A SELECTION OF HEALTH BOOKS

The New Pregnancy and Childbirth Sheila Kitzinger

This new edition of Sheila Kitzinger's classic guide to pregnancy, labour and early parenthood has been fully revised and expanded to take account of the latest medical developments as well as changes in women's attitudes and lifestyles.

Allen Carr's Easyweigh to Lose Weight

Allen Carr's *Easy Way to Stop Smoking* has helped millions of smokers to quit. Now he turns his logical, commonsense approach to food. There are no dos or don'ts, only principles to follow that will lead to healthier eating, greater well-being and permanent weight loss.

Instant Calm Paul Wilson

Contains over a hundred of the most calming techniques known, from the wisdom of ancient civilizations to the discoveries of modern research. 'Every so often you come across a book with the power and insight to transform your life – *Instant Calm* is such a book' Bryce Courtenay

Medicines: A Guide for Everybody Peter Parish

The use of any medicine is always a balance of benefits and risks – this book will help the reader understand how to extend the benefits and reduce the risks. Completely revised, it is written in ordinary, accessible language for the layperson, and is also indispensable to anyone involved in health care.

Miscarriage Ann Oakley, Ann McPherson and Helen Roberts

One million women worldwide become pregnant every day. At least half of these pregnancies end in miscarriage or stillbirth. But each miscarriage is the loss of a potential baby, and that loss can be painful to adjust to. Here is sympathetic support and up-to-date information on one of the commonest areas of women's reproductive experience.

READ MORE IN PENGUIN

A SELECTION OF HEALTH BOOKS

The Food We Eat Joanna Blythman

'Admirably researched, written with clarity and restraint ... [a] ruthlessly honest assessment of the way in which far too much of our food is produced, processed and marketed' Derek Cooper

Calm at Work Paul Wilson

If you've ever felt under pressure from the daily grind, you'll find relief in *Calm at Work*. Page after page of simple techniques, from daydreaming through to negotiation, will help you to add calm, overcome stress and get what you want from your work.

Your Baby and Child Penelope Leach

Completely rewritten and updated, this classic guide to child care and development will become the bible for a new generation of parents. It encompasses the latest research on child development and learning, and reflects changing lifestyles and new approaches to parenting.

The Effective Way to Stop Drinking Beauchamp Colclough

Beauchamp Colclough is an international authority on drink dependency, a reformed alcoholic, and living proof that today's decision is tomorrow's freedom. Follow the expert advice contained here, and it will help you give up drinking – for good.

The New Our Bodies, Ourselves Angela Phillips and Jill Rakusen
A Health Book by and for Women

Rewritten and expanded to meet the needs of women and men in the 1990s, *The New Our Bodies, Ourselves* has influenced the thinking of a generation.

The Complete New Herbal Richard Mabey

The new bible for herb users. It is authoritative, up-to-date, absorbing to read and hugely informative, with practical, clear sections on cultivation and the uses of herbs in daily life, nutrition and healing.